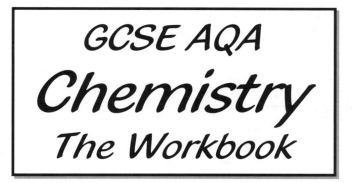

GCSE AQA

Chemistry

The Workbook

This book is for anyone doing **GCSE AQA Chemistry**.
It covers everything you'll need for your year 10 and 11 exams.

It's full of **tricky questions**... each one designed to make you **sweat**
— because that's the only way you'll get any **better**.

There are questions to see **what facts** you know. There are questions
to see how well you can **apply those facts**. And there are questions
to see what you know about **how science works**.

It's also got some daft bits in to try and make the whole
experience at least vaguely entertaining for you.

What CGP is all about

Our sole aim here at CGP is to produce the highest
quality books — carefully written, immaculately presented
and dangerously close to being funny.

Then we work our socks off to get them
out to you — at the cheapest possible prices.

Contents

CHEMISTRY 1A — PRODUCTS FROM ROCKS

Atoms and Elements 1
The Periodic Table 2
Electron Shells 3
Compounds 5
Balancing Equations 6
Using Limestone 8
Getting Metals from Rocks 13
Impacts of Extracting Metals 18
Properties of Metals 19
Alloys 20
Fractional Distillation of Crude Oil 21
Properties and Uses of Crude Oil 22
Using Crude Oil as a Fuel 23
Environmental Problems 24
More Environmental Problems 26
Mixed Questions — Chemistry 1a 30

CHEMISTRY 1B — OILS, EARTH AND ATMOSPHERE

Cracking Crude Oil 34
Alkenes and Ethanol 35
Using Alkenes to Make Polymers 37
Plant Oils 39
Emulsions 41
Plate Tectonics 42
The Earth's Structure 44
The Evolution of the Atmosphere 46
Life, Resources and Atmospheric Change 48
Mixed Questions — Chemistry 1b 50

CHEMISTRY 2A — BONDING AND CALCULATIONS

Atoms, Compounds and Isotopes 53
Ionic Bonding 54
Ions and Formulas 56
Electronic Structure of Ions 57
Covalent Bonding 58
Covalent Substances: Two Kinds 60
Metallic Structures 62
New Materials 64
Polymers 66
Relative Formula Mass 67
Two Formula Mass Calculations 68
Calculating Masses in Reactions 69
Percentage Yield and Reversible Reactions 71
Chemical Analysis and Instrumental Methods 72
Mixed Questions — Chemistry 2a 73

CHEMISTRY 2B — REACTION RATES, SALTS AND ELECTROLYSIS

Rate of Reaction 76
Measuring Rates of Reaction.. 77
Rate of Reaction Experiments.. 79
Collision Theory.. 83
Collision Theory and Catalysts 84
Energy Transfer in Reactions 85
Acids and Alkalis 87
Acids Reacting With Metals 89
Oxides, Hydroxides and Ammonia... 91
Making Salts 93
Electrolysis.. 95
Electrolysis of Sodium Chloride Solution 96
Extraction of Aluminium and Electroplating.. 97
Mixed Questions — Chemistry 2b 98

CHEMISTRY 3A — ELEMENTS, WATER AND ORGANIC CHEMISTRY

History of the Periodic Table... 101
The Modern Periodic Table... 102
Group 1 — The Alkali Metals 104
Group 7 — The Halogens.. 105
Transition Elements 106
Hardness of Water 108
Water Quality 110
Reversible Reactions 111
The Haber Process 113
Alcohols 114
Carboxylic Acids 116
Esters.. 117
Mixed Questions — Chemistry 3a... 118

CHEMISTRY 3B — TITRATIONS, ENERGY AND CHEMICAL TESTS

Titration.. 120
Titration Calculations.. 121
Energy 123
Energy and Fuels 124
Bond Energies... 125
Getting Energy from Hydrogen 127
Tests for Positive Ions 128
Tests for Negative Ions 130
Mixed Questions — Chemistry 3b 131

Published by CGP

From original material by Paddy Gannon.

Editors:
Katherine Craig, Jane Sawers, Karen Wells.

Contributors:
Michael Aicken, Mike Dagless, Ian H Davis, Max Fishel, Rebecca Harvey,
Sidney Stringer Community School, Paul Warren.

ISBN: 978 1 84762 616 5

With thanks to Ellen Bowness, Katie Braid, Chris Elliss, Mary Falkner, Ben Fletcher,
Peter Schofield and Jamie Sinclair for the proofreading.
With thanks to Jan Greenway, Laura Jakubowski and Laura Stoney for the copyright research.

Table of Use of Limestone data on page 10 © East Midlands Aggregates Working Party
Annual Report (via National Stone Centre - publisher).

Groovy website: www.cgpbooks.co.uk

Printed by Elanders Ltd, Newcastle upon Tyne.
Jolly bits of clipart from CorelDRAW®
Based on the classic CGP style created by Richard Parsons.

Atoms and Elements

Q1   **Complete** the following sentences.

a)   Atoms always have a charge of ....

b)   An atom which has lost or gained electrons is called an ....

c)   A neutral atom has the same number of .... and ....

d)   If an electron is added to a neutral atom, the atom becomes .... charged.

Q2   **Complete** this table.

Particle	Charge
Proton	
	0
Electron	

Q3   **What am I?**

Choose from: **nucleus**   **proton**   **electron**   **neutron**

a)   I am in the centre of the atom. I contain protons and neutrons.   ....

b)   I move around the nucleus in a shell.   ....

c)   I am positively charged.   ....

d)   I have no charge.   ....

e)   In a neutral atom there are as many of me as there are electrons.   ....

Q4   Draw a diagram of a **helium** atom.

Label each type of **particle** on your diagram.

Helium has 2 of each type of particle.

Q5   Look at these diagrams of substances. Circle the ones that contain only **one element**.

copper   oxygen   water   ethane

The Periodic Table

Q1   Choose from these words to fill in the blanks.

   left-hand   C   right-hand   horizontal   similar   elements   K
   Cl   different   vertical   metals   P   non-metals   compounds

a)   A group in the periodic table is a .... line of elements.

b)   Most of the elements in the periodic table are ....

c)   There are about 100 different .... in the periodic table.

d)   Non-metals are on the .... side of the periodic table.

e)   Elements in the same group have .... properties.

f)   The symbol for chlorine is .... and the symbol for potassium is ....

Q2   **Sodium** appears in the periodic table as shown below.

23
Na
11

a)   Circle the atomic number on the diagram to the left.

b)   How many protons does Na have? ....

c)   How many electrons does Na have? ....

d)   How many neutrons does Na have? ....

Q3   Elements in the same group undergo **similar reactions**.

a)   Tick the pairs of elements that would undergo similar reactions.

A   potassium and rubidium ☐   C   calcium and oxygen ☐

B   helium and fluorine ☐   D   calcium and magnesium ☐

b)   Explain why sodium and potassium undergo similar reactions with water.

....

....

Q4   **True** or **false**?   **True False**

a)   Group 7 elements are known as the noble gases.   ☐   ☐

b)   All of the noble gases have the same number of electrons in their outer shell.   ☐   ☐

c)   Helium is a noble gas.   ☐   ☐

d)   Noble gases have the maximum number of electrons in their outer energy level.   ☐   ☐

e)   All noble gases are unreactive.   ☐   ☐

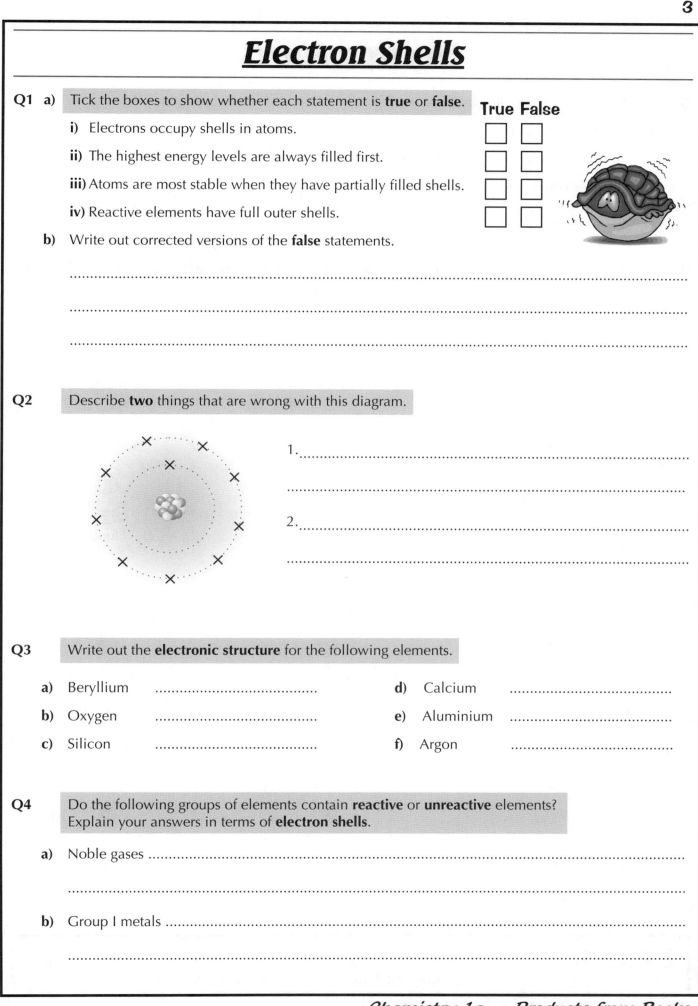

Electron Shells

Q1 a) Tick the boxes to show whether each statement is **true** or **false**.

True False

   i) Electrons occupy shells in atoms. ☐ ☐

   ii) The highest energy levels are always filled first. ☐ ☐

   iii) Atoms are most stable when they have partially filled shells. ☐ ☐

   iv) Reactive elements have full outer shells. ☐ ☐

b) Write out corrected versions of the **false** statements.

....

....

....

Q2 Describe **two** things that are wrong with this diagram.

1. ....

....

2. ....

....

Q3 Write out the **electronic structure** for the following elements.

a) Beryllium ....   **d)** Calcium ....

b) Oxygen ....   **e)** Aluminium ....

c) Silicon ....   **f)** Argon ....

Q4 Do the following groups of elements contain **reactive** or **unreactive** elements? Explain your answers in terms of **electron shells**.

a) Noble gases ....

....

b) Group I metals ....

....

Electron Shells

Q5   **Chlorine** has an atomic number of 17.

a)   What is its electronic structure? ....

b)   Draw the electrons on the shells in the diagram.

c)   Why does chlorine react readily?

....

Q6   Draw the **full electronic structures** for these elements. (The first three have been done for you.)

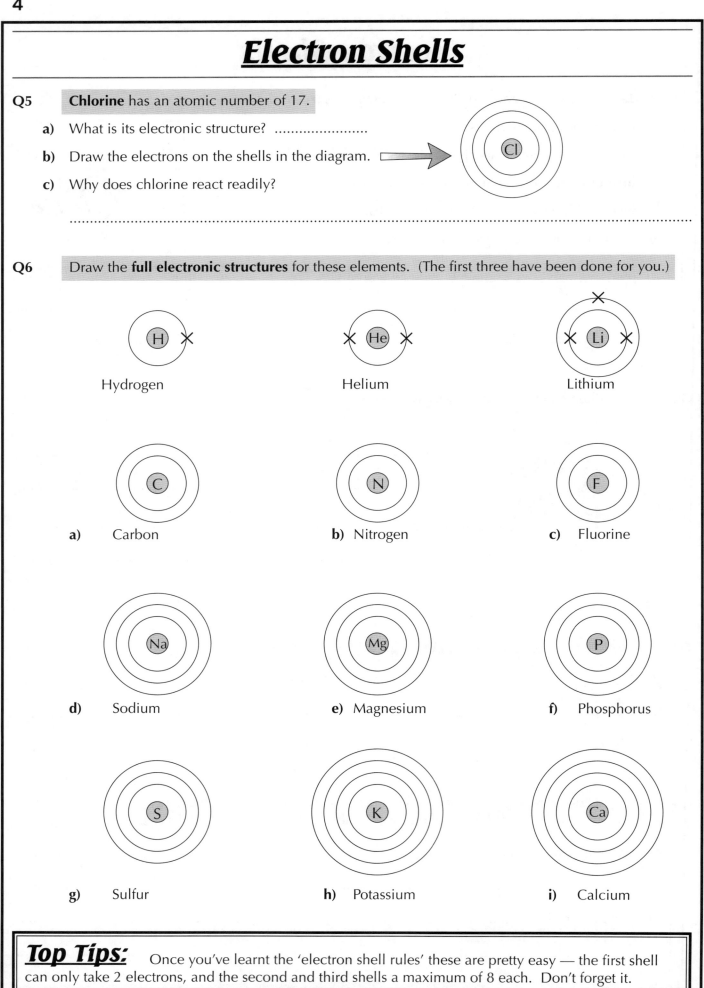

Hydrogen

Helium

Lithium

a)   Carbon

b)   Nitrogen

c)   Fluorine

d)   Sodium

e)   Magnesium

f)   Phosphorus

g)   Sulfur

h)   Potassium

i)   Calcium

Top Tips: Once you've learnt the 'electron shell rules' these are pretty easy — the first shell can only take 2 electrons, and the second and third shells a maximum of 8 each. Don't forget it.

Compounds

Q1 Indicate whether each statement is **true** or **false**.

True False

a) Covalent bonding involves sharing electrons. ☐ ☐

b) Atoms react to gain a full outer shell of electrons. ☐ ☐

c) In ionic bonding, atoms lose or gain electrons. ☐ ☐

d) Ions with opposite charges attract each other. ☐ ☐

Q2 Use the words below to fill in the blanks in the passage.

positive	ionic	molecules	ions	negative	covalent	attracted

A compound which is formed from a metal and a non-metal consists of ....
The metal atoms lose electrons to form .... ions and the non-metal atoms gain
electrons to form .... ions. The opposite charges of the ions mean that they're
strongly .... to each other — called an .... bond. A compound
formed from non-metals consists of .... Each atom shares an electron with
another atom — called a .... bond.

Q3 Use the **diagram** to answer the following questions.

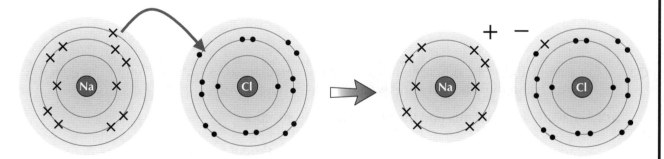

a) What kind of chemical **bond** is shown in the diagram? ....

b) How many **electrons** does **chlorine** need to gain to get a full outer shell of electrons? ....

c) What is the **charge** on a **sodium ion**? ....

d) What is the chemical formula of **sodium chloride**? ....

Q4 Why do some atoms **share** electrons? What **type** of bond do they make?

....

....

Balancing Equations

Q1 Which of the following equations are **balanced** correctly?

		Correctly balanced	Incorrectly balanced
a)	$H_2 + Cl_2 \rightarrow 2HCl$	☐	☐
b)	$CuO + HCl \rightarrow CuCl_2 + H_2O$	☐	☐
c)	$N_2 + H_2 \rightarrow NH_3$	☐	☐
d)	$CuO + H_2 \rightarrow Cu + H_2O$	☐	☐
e)	$CaCO_3 \rightarrow CaO + CO_2$	☐	☐
f)	$CO_2 + H_2O \rightarrow H_2CO_3$	☐	☐

Q2 Here is the equation for the formation of carbon **mon**oxide in a poorly ventilated gas fire. It is **not** balanced correctly.

$$C + O_2 \rightarrow CO$$

Circle the **correctly balanced** version of this equation.

$$C + O_2 \rightarrow CO_2$$
$$C + O_2 \rightarrow 2CO$$
$$2C + O_2 \rightarrow 2CO$$

Q3 In a book, this is the description of a reaction: "**methane** (CH_4) can be burnt in **oxygen** (O_2) to make **carbon dioxide** (CO_2) and **water** (H_2O)".

a) What are the **reactants** and the **products** in this reaction?

Reactants: .... Products: ....

b) Write the **word equation** for this reaction.

....

c) Write the **balanced symbol equation** for the reaction.

....

Don't forget the oxygen ends up in both products

Top Tips: The most important thing to remember with balancing equations is that you can't change the **little numbers** — if you do that then you'll change the substance into something completely different. Just take your time and work through everything logically.

Chemistry 1a — Products from Rocks

Balancing Equations

Q4 Write out the balanced **symbol** equations for the unbalanced picture equations below.

a)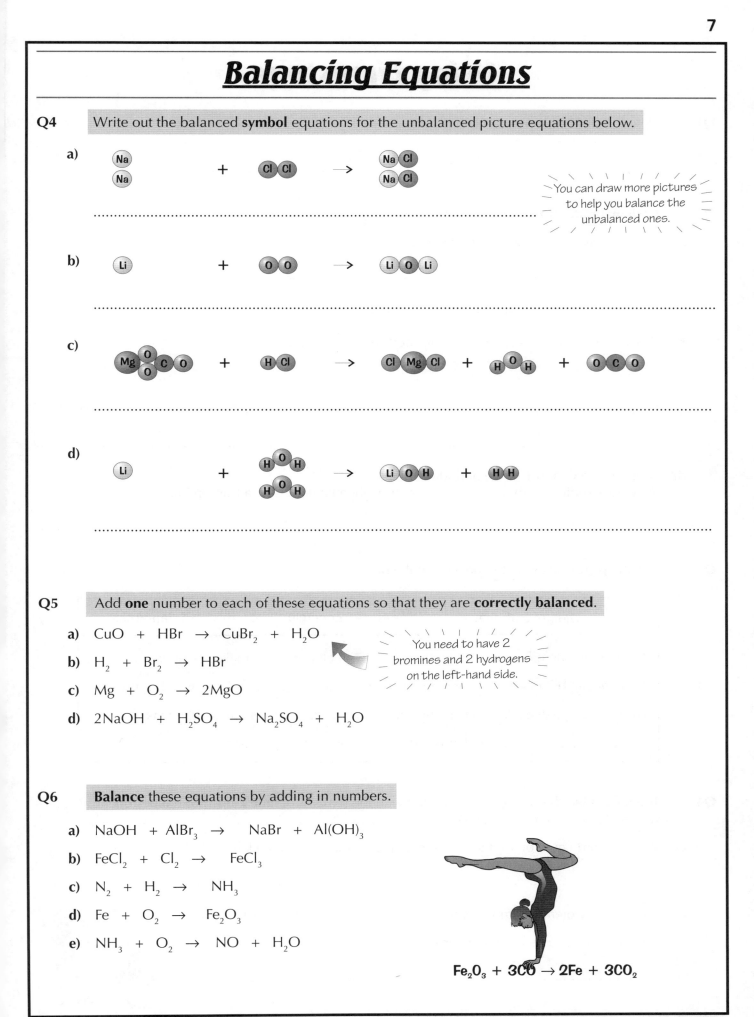

You can draw more pictures to help you balance the unbalanced ones.

....

b)

....

c)

....

d)

....

Q5 Add **one** number to each of these equations so that they are **correctly balanced**.

a) $CuO + HBr \rightarrow CuBr_2 + H_2O$

You need to have 2 bromines and 2 hydrogens on the left-hand side.

b) $H_2 + Br_2 \rightarrow HBr$

c) $Mg + O_2 \rightarrow 2MgO$

d) $2NaOH + H_2SO_4 \rightarrow Na_2SO_4 + H_2O$

Q6 **Balance** these equations by adding in numbers.

a) $NaOH + AlBr_3 \rightarrow NaBr + Al(OH)_3$

b) $FeCl_2 + Cl_2 \rightarrow FeCl_3$

c) $N_2 + H_2 \rightarrow NH_3$

d) $Fe + O_2 \rightarrow Fe_2O_3$

e) $NH_3 + O_2 \rightarrow NO + H_2O$

$Fe_2O_3 + 3CO \rightarrow 2Fe + 3CO_2$

Using Limestone

Q1 State the **chemical name** for limestone.

....

Q2 **Carbonates** decompose to form two products.

a) Name the two products formed when limestone is heated.

1. ....

2. ....

b) What solid would you expect to be formed when magnesium carbonate is heated?

....

c) Write a symbol equation for the reaction that occurs when copper carbonate ($CuCO_3$) is heated.

....

d) Sodium is in Group 1 of the periodic table.
Why does sodium carbonate not decompose when heated using a Bunsen burner?

....

Q3 Use the words below to fill the gaps in the passage.

mortar	sodium carbonate	wood	concrete	clay	limestone

Heating powdered .... with clay in a kiln makes cement.

Cement can be mixed with sand and water to make ...., which is used to

stick bricks together. When cement is mixed with water, gravel and sand it makes

......................................, which is a very common building material.

Q4 The hills of Northern England are dotted with the remains of **lime kilns** where **limestone** ($CaCO_3$) was heated by farmers to make CaO.

a) Write a word equation for the reaction that takes place in a lime kiln.

....

b) CaO reacts violently with water to make calcium hydroxide ($Ca(OH)_2$).

What do farmers use calcium hydroxide for?

....

Using Limestone

Q5 When a carbonate reacts with an acid a **salt** is formed.

a) Complete the **word equation** below to show all the products formed when a carbonate reacts with an acid.

carbonate + acid → salt + ... + ...

b) i) Write the **word equation** for the reaction between **magnesium carbonate** and **sulfuric acid**.

....

ii) Write the **symbol equation** for this reaction.

....

c) Give **two other** examples of carbonates which will react with an acid.

1. ....

2. ....

d) Explain why **limestone buildings** are damaged by acid rain.

....

....

....

....

Q6 **Calcium hydroxide** can be used to test for **carbon dioxide**.

a) Explain why calcium hydroxide can be used in this way.

....

....

....

....

b) Write out the **symbol equation** for the chemical reaction which takes place during this test.

....

Top Tips: Don't get your word and symbol equations mixed up — read the question carefully to make sure you give the right one. If you're asked for a word equation, make sure you use the correct chemical names of the reactant and products. If you're asked for the symbol equation, always double-check that it's balanced correctly or you'll lose valuable marks.

Using Limestone

Q7 Heating metal carbonates is an example of **thermal decomposition**.

a) Explain what **thermal decomposition** means.

....

b) **Calcium oxide** and **calcium carbonate** are both white solids.
How could you tell the difference between them?

Think about what happens when you add calcium oxide to water.

....

Q8 This passage is about **limestone extraction** in the Peak District National Park.
Read the extract and then answer the questions that follow.

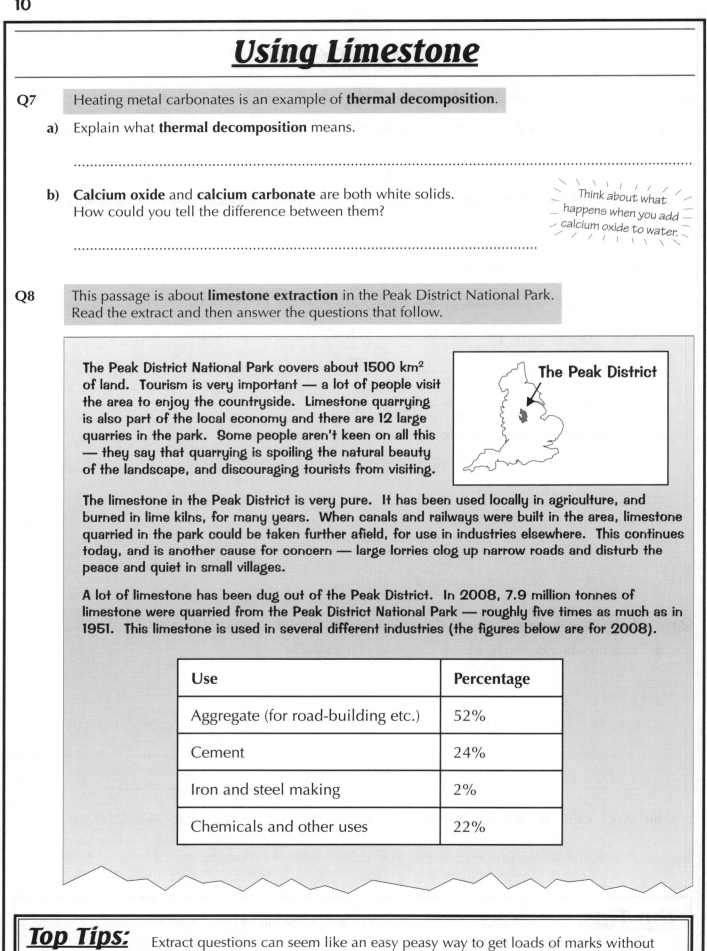

The Peak District National Park covers about 1500 km² of land. Tourism is very important — a lot of people visit the area to enjoy the countryside. Limestone quarrying is also part of the local economy and there are 12 large quarries in the park. Some people aren't keen on all this — they say that quarrying is spoiling the natural beauty of the landscape, and discouraging tourists from visiting.

The Peak District

The limestone in the Peak District is very pure. It has been used locally in agriculture, and burned in lime kilns, for many years. When canals and railways were built in the area, limestone quarried in the park could be taken further afield, for use in industries elsewhere. This continues today, and is another cause for concern — large lorries clog up narrow roads and disturb the peace and quiet in small villages.

A lot of limestone has been dug out of the Peak District. In 2008, 7.9 million tonnes of limestone were quarried from the Peak District National Park — roughly five times as much as in 1951. This limestone is used in several different industries (the figures below are for 2008).

Use	Percentage
Aggregate (for road-building etc.)	52%
Cement	24%
Iron and steel making	2%
Chemicals and other uses	22%

Top Tips: Extract questions can seem like an easy peasy way to get loads of marks without having to really learn anything. But you need to read the extract **carefully** — don't just rush off to answer the questions in an overconfident hurry. That will lead to ridiculous and wrong answers.

Chemistry 1a — Products from Rocks

Using Limestone

a) What makes the **limestone** in the Peak District particularly useful?

....

b) Approximately how many tonnes of limestone were quarried in 1951?

....

c) Give one way in which limestone has been used locally in the Peak District.

....

d) State **three problems** that are caused by quarrying limestone in the Peak District.

1. ....

2. ....

3. ....

e) **i)** How was limestone originally **transported away** from the Peak District?

....

ii) How is limestone **transported** today?

....

f) Do you think that the person who wrote the article is in favour of quarrying or against it? Explain the reasons for your answer.

....

....

g) Complete this table showing the amount of limestone quarried from the Peak District in 2008.

Use	Percentage	Total amount quarried in tonnes
Aggregate (for road-building etc.)	52%	
Cement	24%	
Iron and steel making	2%	
Chemicals and other uses	22%	

Using Limestone

Q9 Many of the products used to build houses are made with limestone.
Circle the materials that have **no** connection to limestone.

paint

bricks

concrete

granite

cement

Q10 In Norway **powdered limestone** is added to lakes that have been damaged by acid rain.

a) Name the process that takes place when the powdered limestone reacts with the acid in the lake.

....

b) Suggest why powdered limestone is also used in the chimneys at power stations.

....

....

....

Q11 Limestone is a useful rock but **quarrying** it causes some **problems**.

a) Describe two problems that quarrying limestone can cause.

1. ....

2. ....

b) Explain how limestone quarries may benefit the local community.

....

....

Q12 What are the **advantages** of using **concrete** instead of these traditional building materials?

a) Wood: ....

b) Metals: ....

c) Bricks: ....

Getting Metals from Rocks

Q1 This table shows some common **metal ores** and their formulas.

Ore	Formula
Haematite	Fe_2O_3
Magnetite	Fe_3O_4
Pyrites	FeS_2
Galena	PbS
Bauxite	Al_2O_3

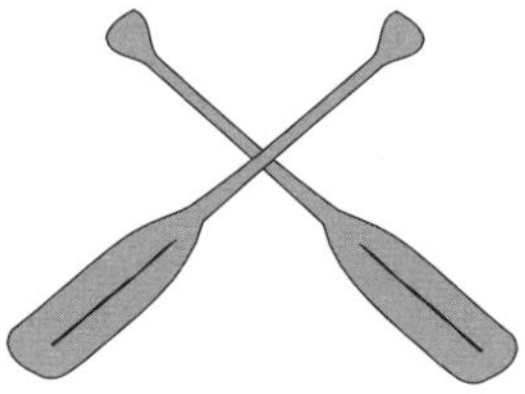

a) What is a metal ore?

....

b) Name the two elements that are commonly bonded to metals in ores.

....

Q2 **Gold** is often extracted from ores that contain very **small** percentages of the metal, but iron is only extracted from ores with a **large** percentage of the metal. Explain why.

....

....

Q3 The graph shows the average **cost** of extracting aluminium over a ten year period.

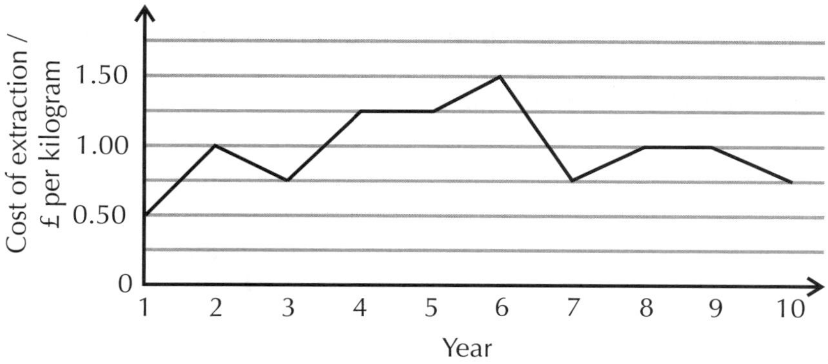

a) In which year was the cost of extracting aluminium **lowest**?

....

b) The cost of mineral extraction per kilogram is 75% of its market value.
In which year was aluminium's market value £2.00 per kilogram?

....

Getting Metals from Rocks

Q4 Explain how improvements in **technology** might affect the economics of metal extraction in future.

....

....

....

Q5 Fill in the blanks in this passage:

.... can be used to extract metals that are .... it in the reactivity series. Oxygen is removed from the metal oxide in a process called .... Other metals have to be extracted using .... because they are .... reactive.

Q6 Imagine that four new metals, **antium**, **bodium**, **candium** and **dekium** have recently been discovered.

Read each of the following statements about the metals.

- Antium is the only one of the four found in the Earth as the metal itself and not as a compound.

- Bodium cannot be extracted by reduction with carbon.

- Candium oxide reacts with carbon to form candium and carbon dioxide.

- Dekium displaces bodium from its oxide.

Use the information above to put the new metals in order of reactivity relative to carbon.

....   **Most reactive**

....

       carbon

....

....   **Least reactive**

Getting Metals from Rocks

Q7 **Copper** is used to make electrical wires.

a) Copper can be extracted from its ore by reduction with carbon.
Suggest why copper produced in this way can't be used for electrical wires.

....

b) i) How is copper that is suitable for making electrical wires produced?

....

ii) Explain one disadvantage of this method.

....

....

Q8 Use the words below to fill in the blanks to complete the paragraph.
Some words may be used more than once.

electrons	electrode	heat	liquid	protons
positive	negative	electricity	copper	

Electrolysis is breaking down a substance using ....

It requires a .... to conduct the

.... During electrolysis, ...

ions move towards the negative ....

Q9 Explain why a substance needs to be either in a **solution** or **molten** for electrolysis to work.

....

....

....

Top Tips: Stuff on the reactivity series isn't easy, so don't worry too much if you found these questions difficult. You don't need to learn the reactivity series off by heart, so spend plenty of time making sure that you understand reduction, electrolysis and displacement reactions.

Getting Metals from Rocks

Q10 Why would it **not** be a good idea to carry out the electrolysis of **copper** in an electrolyte that contained **zinc** ions instead of copper ions? Tick the correct box.

The zinc ions will not conduct an electrical current. ☐

The copper produced will have zinc impurities in it. ☐

A poisonous gas would be produced. ☐

The zinc and copper ions will react with each other. ☐

The zinc ions will coat the anode. ☐

Q11 The diagram below shows the extraction of **copper** by electrolysis.

a) Identify the labels A to C on the diagram.

Choose from the options in the box.

copper ions	copper atoms	copper sulfate solution
	electrodes	batteries

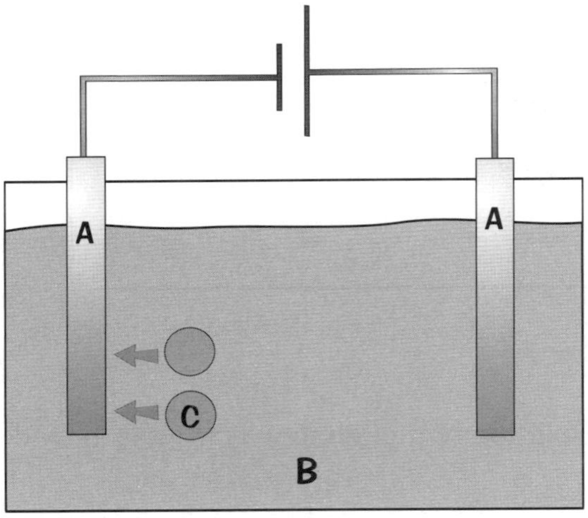

A ....

B ....

C ....

b) When copper is purified by electrolysis, **impure sludge** simply falls to the bottom. It does **not** move to the cathode. Explain why this happens.

....

....

Getting Metals from Rocks

Q12 If scrap iron is heated with copper sulfate this reaction happens:

iron + copper sulfate → copper + iron sulfate

a) Why does this reaction take place? ....

b) Would it be possible to produce iron sulfate by reacting iron with aluminium sulfate? ....

Explain your answer. ....

....

Q13 Copper objects such as old pipes can be **recycled**.
Give **two** reasons why it is important to recycle copper.

1. ....

2. ....

Q14 Scientists are researching **alternative** methods of extracting copper.
Bioleaching is one alternative method which can be used.

a) **Explain** how bioleaching can be used to extract **copper** from copper sulfide.

....

....

....

....

b) Give **another** example of an alternative extraction method used for copper.

....

c) Explain why these alternative extraction methods are so important.

....

....

....

....

18

__Impacts of Extracting Metals__

Q1 New mines always have **social**, **economic** and **environmental** consequences.
Complete this table to show the effects that a new mine can have.

Social	Economic	Environmental
Services, e.g. health care may be improved because of influx of people.		Pollution from traffic.

Remember to include both positive and negative effects.

Q2 Wherever possible, every scrap of gold is **recycled**. We also recycle **aluminium** as much as possible, even though it is the most common metal in the Earth's crust. Explain the reasons why we **recycle** these two metals.

....

....

....

....

__Top Tips:__ Remember that metals are finite resources — there's a set amount on Earth and once we've extracted them all there won't be any more. We need to be able to get metals out of low-grade ores (ones that only contain small amounts of metal) to get enough to go round.

Chemistry 1a — Products from Rocks

Properties of Metals

Q1 This table shows some of the **properties** of four different **metals**.

Metal	Heat conduction	Cost	Resistance to corrosion	Strength
1	average	high	excellent	good
2	average	medium	good	excellent
3	excellent	low	good	good
4	low	high	average	poor

Use the information in the table to choose which metal
would be **best** for making each of the following:

a) Saucepan bases ....

b) Car bodies ....

c) A statue to be placed in a town centre ....

*Think about how
long a statue would
have to last for.*

Q2 What **properties** does copper have that make it suitable for use in **plumbing**?

....

....

Q3 a) **Aluminium** and **titanium** are similar in some ways but different in others.
Complete this table to compare the properties of **aluminium** with those of **titanium**.

Property	Aluminium	Titanium
Density		
Strength	low	high
Corrosion resistance		

b) Which of the two metals would be more suitable for making artificial hip joints?

....

Alloys

Q1 Most iron is made into the alloy **steel**.

a) Write a definition of the term 'alloy'.

....

....

b) How is **iron** turned into **steel**?

....

Tonight Matthew, I'm going to be... steel.

....

Q2 a) Draw lines to connect the correct phrases in each column. One has been done for you.

Metal / Alloy	What has been added	Use
low-carbon steel	nothing	blades for tools
iron from a blast furnace	chromium	cutlery
high-carbon steel	0.1% carbon	car bodies
stainless steel	1.5% carbon	ornamental railings

b) Why does iron from a **blast furnace** have few uses?

....

Q3 24-carat gold is **pure** gold. 9-carat gold contains **9 parts** gold to 15 parts other metals. 9-carat gold is **harder** and **cheaper** than 24-carat gold.

What percentage of 9-carat gold is actually gold?

....

Top Tips: Alloys are all about bending metals to your will and getting them to do what you want. Make a friendly alloy of the examiner and you're sure to get a good mark in the exam. Do it by learning all the wonderful things you can get iron to do by making different alloys with it.

Fractional Distillation of Crude Oil

Q1 Circle the correct words to complete these sentences.

   a) Crude oil is a **mixture / compound** of different molecules.

   b) Most of the compounds in crude oil are **carbohydrate / hydrocarbon** molecules.

   c) The molecules in crude oil **are / aren't** chemically bonded to each other.

   d) Physical methods **can / can't** be used to separate out the molecules in crude oil.

Q2 The molecules listed below are in the order of **smallest** to **largest** from left to right. Label this diagram of a **fractionating column** to show where these substances can be collected.

petrol   kerosene   diesel   oil   bitumen

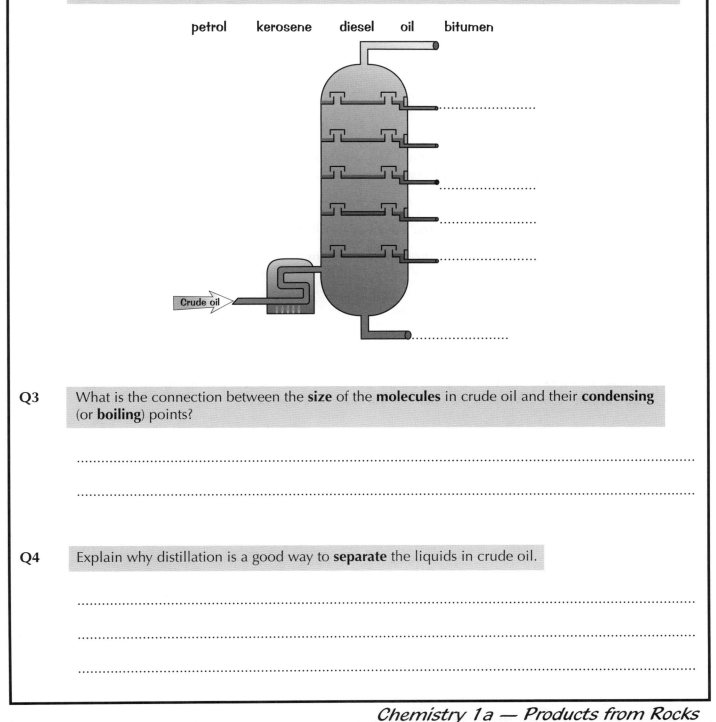

Q3 What is the connection between the **size** of the **molecules** in crude oil and their **condensing** (or **boiling**) points?

....

....

Q4 Explain why distillation is a good way to **separate** the liquids in crude oil.

....

....

....

Properties and Uses of Crude Oil

Q1   **Crude oil** is a mixture of **hydrocarbons**. These **hydrocarbons** are mostly **alkanes**.

a)   Draw the structures of the first three alkanes and name each alkane you have drawn.

1.   2.   3.

....

b)   Which of these alkanes would you expect to have the highest boiling point?

....

Q2   There are some basic **trends** in the way that **alkanes** behave.
Circle the correct words to complete these sentences.

a)   The longer the alkane molecule the **more / less** viscous (gloopy) it is.

b)   The shorter the alkane molecule the **lower / higher** its boiling point.

c)   The shorter the alkane molecule the **more / less** flammable it is.

Q3 a)   What is the **general** formula for **alkanes**?

If you can't remember it you can work it out by looking at the diagrams you have drawn at the top of the page.

....

b)   **Eicosane** is a hydrocarbon that can be used to make candles. Each molecule of eicosane contains **20 carbon** atoms. What is the **chemical formula** for eicosane?

....

Q4   Each hydrocarbon molecule in engine oil has a **long** string of carbon atoms.

a)   Explain why this type of oil is good for using as a **lubricant** in an engine.

....

b)   Engines get very **hot** when they are in use. Why would oil molecules with short carbon chains be unsuitable for use as lubricants?

....

....

Using Crude Oil as a Fuel

Q1 As crude oil is a **non-renewable** resource people are keen to find **alternative** energy sources. Suggest a problem with each of these ways of using alternative fuels.

a) **Solar** energy for cars: ....

b) **Wind** energy to power an oven: ....

c) **Nuclear** energy for buses: ....

Q2 Forty years ago some scientists predicted that there would be no oil left by the year 2000, but obviously they were **wrong**. One reason is that modern engines are more **efficient** than ones in the past, so they use less fuel. Give two other reasons why the scientists' prediction was wrong.

....

....

Q3 Using oil products as fuels causes some **environmental** problems. Explain the environmental problems that are associated with each of the following:

a) **Transporting** crude oil across the sea in tankers.

....

b) **Burning** oil products to release the energy they contain.

....

....

....

Q4 Write a short paragraph summarising why crude oil is the most **common source** of fuel even though **alternatives** are available.

....

....

....

....

Environmental Problems

Q1   Draw lines to link the correct parts of these sentences.

The main cause of acid rain is	acid rain.
Acid rain kills trees and	sulfuric acid.
Sulfur dioxide is produced by burning fuels which contain	acidifies lakes.
Limestone buildings and statues are affected by	sulfur dioxide.
In clouds sulfur dioxide reacts with water to make	sulfur.

Q2   Give **two** ways that the amount of **acid rain** can be reduced.

1. ....

....

2. ....

....

Q3   **Exhaust** fumes from cars and lorries often contain **carbon monoxide** and **carbon particles**.

a)   Why are they more likely to be formed in **engines** than if the fuel was burnt in the open air?

....

....

b)   Give one **problem** associated with carbon monoxide.

....

Top Tips: The best way to prevent acid rain damage is to reduce the amount of sulfur dioxide that we release into the atmosphere. When acid rain does fall there are some ways of reducing the amount of damage it causes, such as adding powdered limestone to affected lakes.

Environmental Problems

Q4 a) Tick the boxes to indicate whether each statement is **true** or **false**.

		True	False
i)	All fuels produce carbon dioxide when burnt.	☐	☐
ii)	When a fuel burns in an excess of oxygen, it's called complete combustion.	☐	☐
iii)	Particulates are released when fossil fuels undergo partial combustion.	☐	☐
iv)	Oxides of nitrogen form if a fuel burns at low temperatures.	☐	☐
v)	Soot forms if a fuel contains sulfur.	☐	☐

b) Write out the **correct** versions of the **false** statements.

....

....

....

....

Q5 a) Write a word equation for completely **burning** a **hydrocarbon** in the open air.

....

b) Write **balanced symbol equations** for completely burning these alkanes in open air:

i) methane:

....

ii) propane:

....

Q6 **Partial combustion** can cause problems.

a) Fill in the blanks to complete the word equation for the partial combustion of a hydrocarbon.

hydrocarbon + ... →

water + carbon dioxide + ... + ...

b) Why is partial combustion messy?

....

....

More Environmental Problems

Q1 Look at the graph and then answer the questions below.

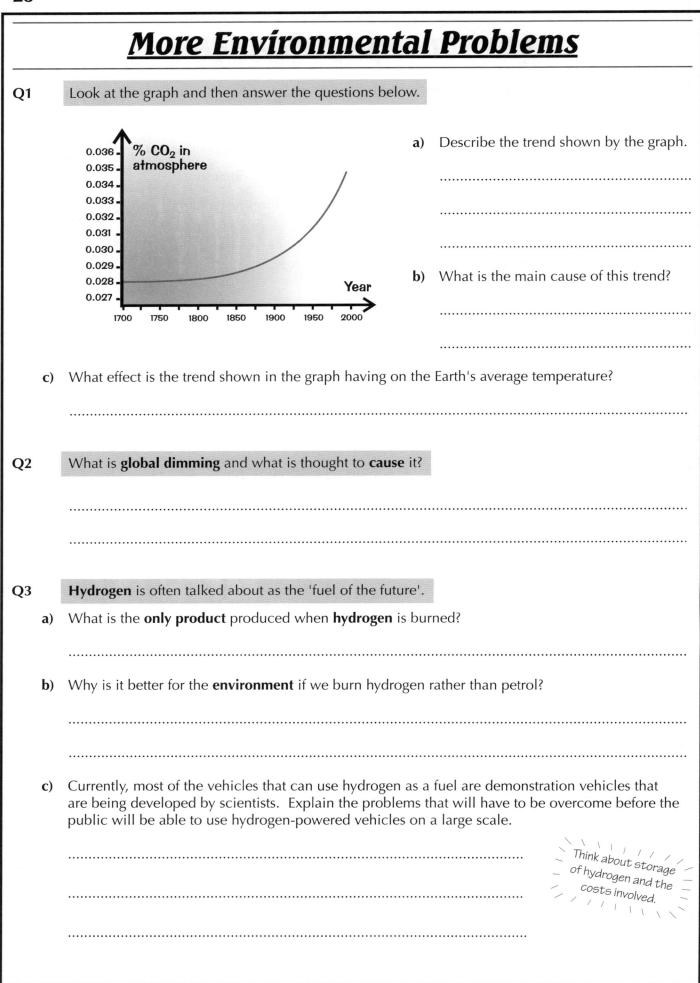

a) Describe the trend shown by the graph.

....

....

....

b) What is the main cause of this trend?

....

....

c) What effect is the trend shown in the graph having on the Earth's average temperature?

....

Q2 What is **global dimming** and what is thought to **cause** it?

....

....

Q3 **Hydrogen** is often talked about as the 'fuel of the future'.

a) What is the **only product** produced when **hydrogen** is burned?

....

b) Why is it better for the **environment** if we burn hydrogen rather than petrol?

....

....

c) Currently, most of the vehicles that can use hydrogen as a fuel are demonstration vehicles that are being developed by scientists. Explain the problems that will have to be overcome before the public will be able to use hydrogen-powered vehicles on a large scale.

Think about storage of hydrogen and the costs involved.

....

....

....

More Environmental Problems

Q4   In Brazil **ethanol** produced by **fermenting** sugar cane is a popular fuel for vehicles.
The ethanol is mixed with **petrol** before it is used.

   a)   What products are produced when **ethanol** (C_2H_5OH) is completely burnt?

   ....

   b)   Give **one** problem with the use of **ethanol** as a fuel.

   ....

Q5   Biodiesel is a fuel made from vegetable oil.
A litre of biodiesel contains **90%** of the energy found in a litre of normal diesel.

   Normal diesel contains 37 megajoules (37 000 000 J) of energy per litre.
How much energy does a litre of biodiesel contain?

   ....

   ....

Q6   Scientists are working hard to develop new **technologies** that are **environmentally friendly**.

   a)   List some ways that people can alter their lifestyles so that they cause less environmental damage.

   ....

   ....

   ....

   b)   Do you think it is solely the responsibility of scientists to find ways of reducing environmental
damage or should people be prepared to change their lifestyles too? Explain your answer.

   ....

   ....

   ....

   ....

   ....

   ....

Top Tips: If a question asks you what you think, you can say whatever you want (as long
as it answers the question) but you'll have to back up your argument by saying **why** you think that.
The examiner is looking for your **reasons** so make sure they're logical and realistic.

More Environmental Problems

Q7   Biodiesel is said to be "carbon neutral".

a)   Explain why this is.

....

....

b)   Why is normal diesel not carbon neutral?

....

....

....

Q8   Read this passage and answer the questions on the **next page**.

Biodiesel is a liquid fuel which can be made from vegetable oils. It's renewable, and can be used instead of ordinary diesel in cars and lorries. It can also be blended with normal diesel — this is common in some countries, such as France. You don't have to modify your car's engine to use biodiesel.

Biodiesel has several advantages. Producing and using it releases 80% less carbon dioxide overall than producing and using fossil-fuel diesel. So if we want to do something about climate change, using biodiesel would be a good start. Biodiesel is also less harmful if it's accidentally spilled, because it's readily biodegradable.

In the UK, we make most of our biodiesel from recycled cooking oils. But we don't make very much yet — you can only buy it from about 100 filling stations. The Government has been making some effort to encourage us to use more biodiesel. There's one major problem — it's about twice as expensive to make as ordinary diesel.

Most of the price you pay for petrol or diesel is not the cost of the fuel — it's tax, which goes straight to the Government. Over the last decade, the Government has increased fuel taxes, making petrol and diesel more expensive to buy. Part of the reason they've done this is to try to put us off buying them — because burning fossil fuels releases harmful pollutants and contributes to climate change.

So, to make biodiesel cheaper, in 2002, the Government cut the tax rate on it. The tax on biodiesel is now 20p/litre less than it is on normal diesel. This makes biodiesel a similar price to normal diesel. If the Government cuts the tax even further, then more people would be keen to use biodiesel, and more filling stations would start to sell it.

Pay less tax — buy biodiesel

More Environmental Problems

a) In the UK, what do we produce most of our biodiesel from at present?

....

b) What would the environmental impact be if biodiesel was more widely used?

....

....

....

c) What has the Government done to encourage people to switch from normal diesel to biodiesel?

....

....

....

d) If lots more people start buying biodiesel instead of normal diesel, what problem is this likely to cause for the Government?

....

....

e)

> "I don't want to change to biodiesel. I don't want all the hassle of getting my car modified, and biodiesel costs more. It's just another way for the Government to get money off the taxpayers."

Write a response to this using information from the passage on the previous page.

....

....

....

....

....

Mixed Questions — Chemistry 1a

Q1 Metals make up about 80% of all the elements in the periodic table.

a) Shade the area where **metals** are found on this periodic table:

b) Read each of the following statements about metals. If the statement is **true**, tick the box.

☐ Metals are generally strong but also malleable.

☐ All metals are corrosion-resistant.

☐ Metals conduct electricity well.

☐ Generally, metals are poor conductors of heat.

☐ Properties of a metal can be altered by mixing it with another metal to form an alloy.

c) Look at the information in the table below. R, S, T and U are all metals.

Material	Strength	Cost (£)	Density (g/cm³)	Melting Point (°C)
R	High	100	3	1000
S	Medium	90	5	150
T	High	450	8	1200
U	Low	200	11	1070

Explain in detail which material would be most suitable to build an **aeroplane body**.

....

....

....

....

Q2 The extraction, transportation and processing of crude oil is a major industry.

a) Name one product of the crude oil industry, other than a fuel.

....

b) Name one problem associated with the **transportation** of crude oil.

....

Mixed Questions — Chemistry 1a

Q3 The metals **aluminium**, **copper** and **iron** can be extracted from their ores.

a) Metal ores are often described as 'finite resources'. Explain the term '**finite resource**'.

....

b) The table shows the **reactivity** series of metals and **dates of discovery**.

i) What pattern can be seen in the data?

....

....

ii) Suggest an explanation for this.

....

....

....

....

metal	discovery
potassium	AD 1807
sodium	AD 1807
calcium	AD 1808
magnesium	AD 1755
aluminium	AD 1825
carbon	
zinc	about AD 1400
iron	about 2500 BC
tin	about 2000 BC
lead	about 3500 BC
hydrogen	
copper	about 4200 BC
silver	about 4000 BC
gold	about 6000 BC
platinum	before 1500 BC

most reactive ↑ ↓ least reactive

c) **i)** Complete the word equation for the reduction of iron ore with carbon.

iron(III) oxide + ... → **iron** + ...

ii) Write a **balanced symbol equation** for this reaction. (The formula of iron(III) oxide is Fe_2O_3.)

....

d) Copper metal can be extracted from its ore by **reduction** using carbon then purified by electrolysis.

i) Explain why electrolysis is used to produce copper metal for **electrical wiring**.

....

ii) Give **two** physical properties of copper that make it suitable for use in **electrical wiring**.

1. ....

2. ....

e) One of the most common elements present in the Earth's crust is aluminium. Explain why aluminium metal can only be extracted using **electrolysis**.

....

....

....

Mixed Questions — Chemistry 1a

Q4 **Petrol** and **diesel** are two commonly used fuels for cars.

a) Diesel has longer molecules than petrol.
List **three** differences you would expect in physical properties between petrol and diesel.

1. ....

2. ....

3. ....

b) **Ethanol** is an alternative fuel to petrol and diesel.

i) How can ethanol be produced? ....

ii) Why is ethanol a more environmentally friendly fuel?

....

Q5 **Lubricating oils** in car engines keep moving metal surfaces apart. Viscous oils do this better than runny oils, but if they're too viscous they don't lubricate the moving parts properly.

The following experiment was set up to find which of two oils was the more viscous.
The time taken for each oil to run through the burette was noted at two temperatures.

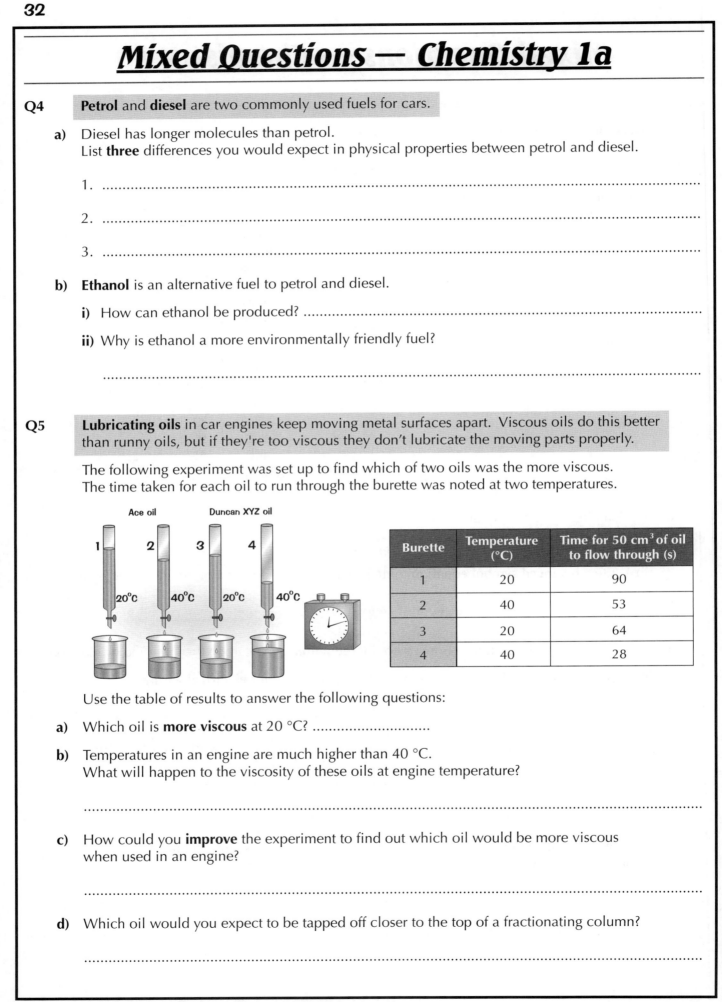

Burette	Temperature (°C)	Time for 50 cm³ of oil to flow through (s)
1	20	90
2	40	53
3	20	64
4	40	28

Use the table of results to answer the following questions:

a) Which oil is **more viscous** at 20 °C? ....

b) Temperatures in an engine are much higher than 40 °C.
What will happen to the viscosity of these oils at engine temperature?

....

c) How could you **improve** the experiment to find out which oil would be more viscous when used in an engine?

....

d) Which oil would you expect to be tapped off closer to the top of a fractionating column?

....

Mixed Questions — Chemistry 1a

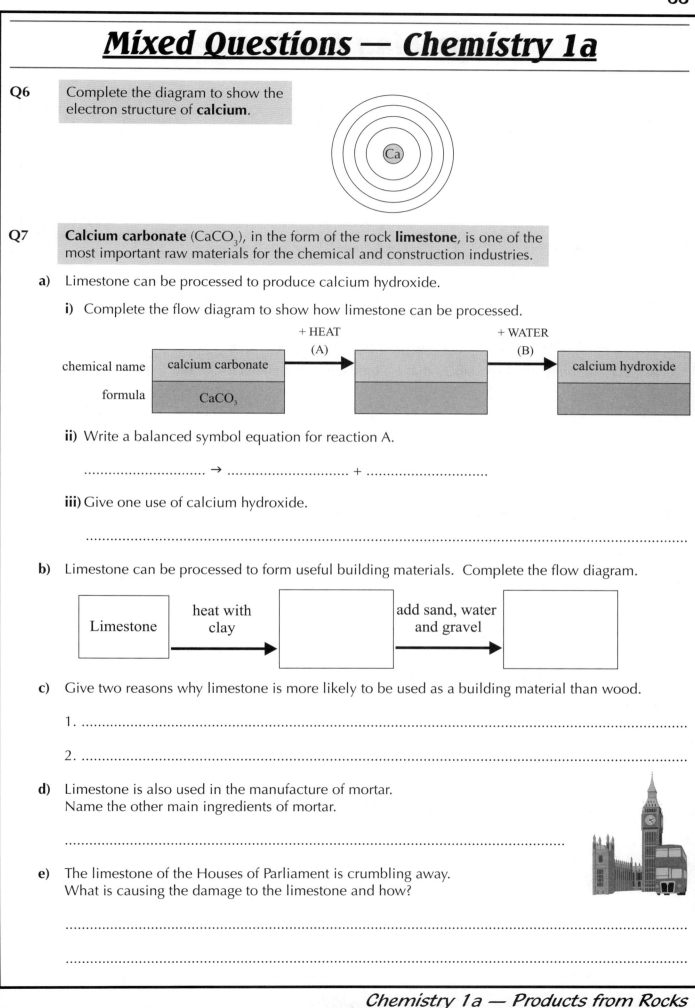

Q6 Complete the diagram to show the electron structure of **calcium**.

Q7 **Calcium carbonate** ($CaCO_3$), in the form of the rock **limestone**, is one of the most important raw materials for the chemical and construction industries.

a) Limestone can be processed to produce calcium hydroxide.

   i) Complete the flow diagram to show how limestone can be processed.

	+ HEAT (A)		+ WATER (B)	
chemical name	calcium carbonate			calcium hydroxide
formula	$CaCO_3$			

   ii) Write a balanced symbol equation for reaction A.

   .... → .... + ...

   iii) Give one use of calcium hydroxide.

   ....

b) Limestone can be processed to form useful building materials. Complete the flow diagram.

Limestone	heat with clay		add sand, water and gravel	

c) Give two reasons why limestone is more likely to be used as a building material than wood.

   1. ....

   2. ....

d) Limestone is also used in the manufacture of mortar. Name the other main ingredients of mortar.

   ....

e) The limestone of the Houses of Parliament is crumbling away. What is causing the damage to the limestone and how?

   ....

   ....

Cracking Crude Oil

Q1 Fill in the gaps with the words below.

high	shorter	long	catalyst	cracking	diesel	molecules	petrol

There is more need for .... chain fractions of crude oil such

as .... than for longer chains such as ....

Heating .... hydrocarbon molecules to ....

temperatures with a .... breaks them down into smaller

.... This is called ....

Q2 Diesel is **cracked** to produce products that are more in demand.

a) Suggest three useful substances that are produced when diesel is cracked.

....

b) What type of reaction is cracking?

....

Q3 After cracking both **alkenes** and **alkanes** are present.

a) Bromine water is used to test whether a substance is an alkane or alkene.
Alkenes decolourise bromine water, but alkanes don't.

Which of the following would decolourise bromine water?

☐ propane   ☐ ethene   ☐ ethane

b) Put the steps of the cracking process in the correct order by writing numbers in the boxes.

☐ The vapour is passed over a catalyst at a high temperature.

☐ The long-chain molecules are heated.

☐ The molecules are cracked on the surface of the catalyst.

☐ They are vaporised (turned into a gas).

Q4 Change this diagram into a **word equation** and a **symbol equation**.

a) Word equation: .... → .... + ...

b) Symbol equation: .... → .... + ...

Alkenes and Ethanol

Q1 Complete this table showing the molecular and displayed formulas of some alkenes.

Alkene	Formula	Displayed formula
Ethene	a)	b)
c)	C_3H_6	d)

The displayed formula just shows how all the atoms are arranged.

Q2 The general formula for alkenes is C_nH_{2n}. Use it to write down the formulas of these alkenes.

a) pentene (5 carbons) ....

b) hexene (6 carbons) ....

c) octene (8 carbons) ....

d) dodecene (12 carbons) ....

Q3 True or false?

		True	False
a)	Alkenes have double bonds between the hydrogen atoms.	☐	☐
b)	Alkenes are unsaturated.	☐	☐
c)	Alkenes are not very useful.	☐	☐
d)	Ethene has two carbon atoms.	☐	☐

Q4 Fill in the gaps with the words below. You might need to use some words more than once.

orange	bromine water	colourless	decolourise

You can test for alkenes by adding them to ....

An alkene will .... the ...., turning it from

.... to ....

Alkenes and Ethanol

Q5   There are two ways of making ethanol:

> **Method A**   Sugar → ethanol + carbon dioxide
>
> **Method B**   Ethene + steam → ethanol

a)   Which of the methods describes making ethanol by **fermentation**? ....

b)   Draw lines to match up the boxes.

Method A		Uses a catalyst

Method B		Uses yeast

c)   Ethanol can be used as a fuel. In some countries the fermentation method is often used to produce it. Give two reasons why this method is chosen.

1. ....

2. ....

d)   Give a disadvantage of the fermentation method.

....

....

Q6   Explain why producing ethanol from ethene could become **problematic** in the future.

....

....

....

....

Top Tips: It's a cracking idea getting alkenes from crude oil because they're pretty useful for making things, like ethanol. You probably wouldn't want to drink the ethanol you get from reacting ethene with steam though. On the other hand, the ethanol you get from fermenting sugar is pretty multipurpose — it's good for anything from your old man's pint to fuelling his car.

Using Alkenes to Make Polymers

Q1 Tick the box next to the **true** statement below.

☐ The monomer of poly(ethene) is ethene.

☐ The polymer of poly(ethene) is ethane.

☐ The monomer of poly(ethene) is ethane.

We bring you gold, frankincense...
and poly-myrrh

Q2 Polymers have many uses, for example, in LYCRA® fibre for tights.

Give three other uses of polymers.

1. ....

2. ....

3. ....

Q3 Most polymers are **not** biodegradable.

Biodegradable means that something can rot.

a) What problems does this cause for the environment?

....

....

b) How can you minimise this environmental problem when using objects made from polymers?

....

....

c) Things are often made from plastics because they are cheap. Why might this change in the future?

....

Think about what
plastics are made from.

....

....

Using Alkenes to Make Polymers

Q4   The equation below shows the polymerisation of ethene to form **poly(ethene)**.

$$n \begin{pmatrix} H & H \\ | & | \\ C = C \\ | & | \\ H & H \end{pmatrix} \longrightarrow \begin{pmatrix} H & H \\ | & | \\ C - C \\ | & | \\ H & H \end{pmatrix}_n$$

many ethene molecules   **poly(ethene)**

Draw a similar equation below to show the polymerisation of propene (C_3H_6).

It's easier if you think of propene as

$$\begin{array}{c} H \\ \diagdown \\ C = C \\ \diagup \\ H \end{array} \begin{array}{c} H \\ \diagup \\ \diagdown \\ CH_3 \end{array}$$

Q5   Plastic bags made just from polymers don't biodegrade.

Name two materials that can now be combined to make biodegradable plastic bags.

1. ....

2. ....

Q6   Fractional distillation of crude oil produces useful fractions and not-so-useful fractions. The not-so-useful ones are **cracked** to form alkenes. Alkenes can be **polymerised** to make plastics.

Write down the differences between cracking and polymerisation.

....

....

....

....

Top Tips: It's amazingly easy to name polymers. You just take the name of the monomer (the little molecules that are joined together) stick it in brackets, and write the word 'poly' in front of it. And Bob's your uncle (except if his name's Mike or anything else that's not Bob).

Plant Oils

Q1   Oil can be extracted from some **fruits** and **seeds**.

a)   Name two fruits and two seeds which are good sources of oil.

Fruits: .... and ....

Seeds: .... and ....

b)   Give two uses of plant oils.

1. ....

2. ....

c)   Why is the use of high pressure an important part of the oil extraction process?

....

Q2   Write out a **correct version** of this sentence.

Vegetable oils provide loads of energy, but are not nutritious.

....

....

Q3   Tick the boxes to show whether these statements are true or false.

		True	False
a)	Vegetable oils have lower boiling points than water.	☐	☐
b)	Vegetable oils help food cook faster.	☐	☐
c)	Cooking with vegetable oils reduces the energy content of food.	☐	☐
d)	Flavours come from chemicals that are soluble in oil.	☐	☐
e)	Food cooked in oils has less flavour.	☐	☐

Q4   Vegetable oils can be turned into **fuels**.

a)   Explain why vegetable oils are suitable for processing into fuels.

....

b)   Name one fuel made from vegetable oil.

....

Plant Oils

Q5 Ben and Martin both planned an experiment to identify saturated and unsaturated oils.

Ben's Method

1. Put some oil in a test tube.
2. Add some bromine water.
3. Shake vigorously.
4. Repeat for next oil.
5. When all the oils are done, write down the results.

Martin's Method

1. Put 2 ml of oil into a test tube.
2. Label the test tube with the name of the oil sample.
3. Add 5 drops of bromine water.
4. Record any colour change.
5. Repeat for each oil.

Whose experimental method is better? Give reasons for your answer.

....

....

....

Q6 Margarine is usually made from partially hydrogenated vegetable oil.

a) Describe the process of hydrogenation.

....

....

b) How does hydrogenation affect the melting points of vegetable oils?

....

c) Explain why some vegetable oils are only partially hydrogenated.
Give an example of a partially hydrogenated vegetable oil.

....

....

Q7 Some types of fats are considered bad for your heart.

a) Which type of fats are **less healthy**? Underline your answer.

Saturated   **Unsaturated**

b) Explain why this type of fat is bad for your heart.

....

....

Emulsions

Q1 Each of these sentences has an error. Write out a **correct version** of each sentence.

a) Emulsions are always formed from oil suspended in water.

....

b) The thicker an emulsion, the less oil it contains.

....

c) Emulsions can be combined with air, but it makes them runnier.

....

Air is whipped into cream to make a topping for a trifle.

d) Emulsions are only found in foods.

....

Q2 **Lecithin** is added to chocolate drinks to prevent the oils separating out from the water. The diagram shows a molecule of lecithin.

a) Label the **hydrophilic** part and the **hydrophobic** part of the lecithin molecule.

b) Explain how this molecule keeps the oil and water parts of chocolate drinks from separating into two different layers. Include a diagram to help explain your answer.

....

....

....

....

....

....

Q3 Adding emulsifiers to foods has **advantages** and **disadvantages**.

a) Explain why emulsifiers increase the shelf-life of food.

....

b) Why can adding emulsifiers to food sometimes be problematic?

....

....

Chemistry 1b — Oils, Earth and Atmosphere

Plate Tectonics

Q1 Below is a letter that Alfred Wegener might have written to a newspaper explaining his ideas. Use your knowledge to fill in the gaps.

Dear Herr Schmidt,

I must reply to your highly flawed article of March 23rd 1915 by telling you of my theory of .... Finally I can explain why the .... of identical plants and animals have been found in seemingly unconnected places such as .... and ....

The current idea of sunken .... between these continents is complete hogwash. I propose that South America and Africa were once part of a much larger land mass that I have named .... This supercontinent has slowly been drifting apart over millions of years. The pieces are being pushed by tidal forces and the .... of the Earth itself.

I will shortly be publishing a full report of my scientific findings.

Yours faithfully,
A Wegener

Q2 True or false?

	True	False
Wegener found that each continent had its own unrelated collection of plant and animal fossils.	☐	☐
Animals were thought to have crossed between continents using land bridges.	☐	☐
The Earth's continents seem to fit together like a big jigsaw.	☐	☐
Rocks are made of layers, which are different on every continent.	☐	☐
Fossils of tropical plants have been found in places where they shouldn't have survived, like the Arctic.	☐	☐
Pangaea is thought to have existed 3 million years ago.	☐	☐
Most scientists immediately agreed with Wegener's ideas.	☐	☐
Wegener had studied geology.	☐	☐
Investigations of the ocean floor showed that although Wegener wasn't absolutely right, his ideas were pretty close.	☐	☐
Wegener died before his ideas were accepted.	☐	☐

Plate Tectonics

Q3   Wegener's theory of continental drift was put forward after he found **evidence**. List four pieces of evidence that Wegener found.

1. ....

....

2. ....

....

3. ....

....

4. ....

....

....

Q4   According to Wegener's theory, the continents were moving apart.

a) **i)** What two forces did Wegener suggest were responsible for the movement of the continents?

....

ii) Why did many scientists say that this was impossible?

....

....

iii) Give two other reasons why most scientists weren't convinced by Wegener's theory.

....

....

b) Where did scientists finally find evidence that supported Wegener's ideas?

....

....

The Earth's Structure

Q1 Look at the diagram showing the boundary between the African and Arabian plates.

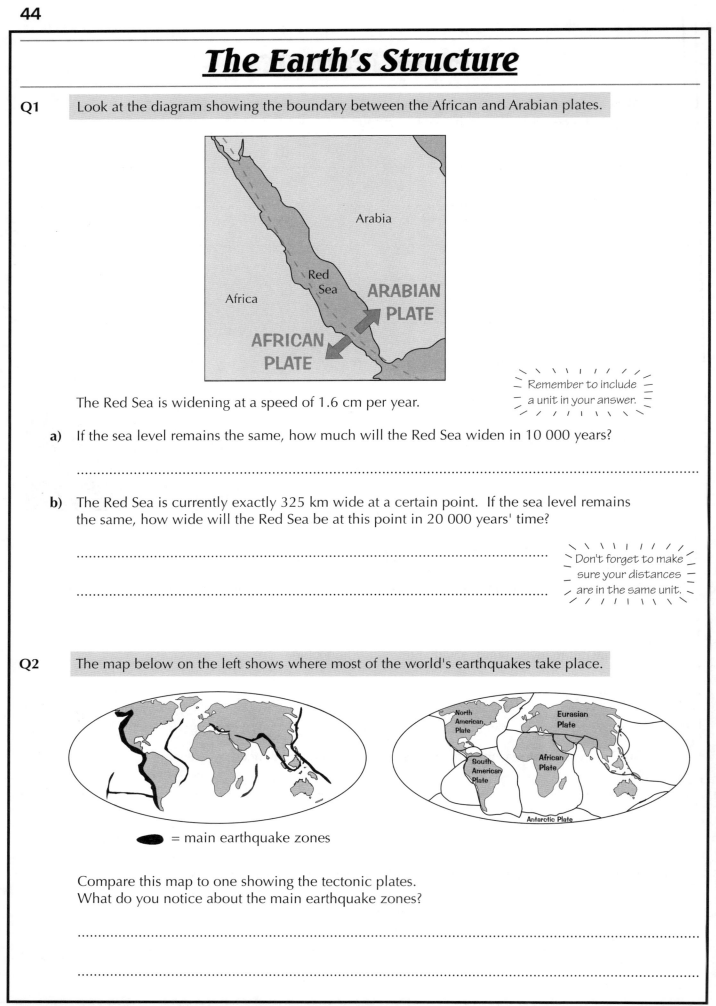

The Red Sea is widening at a speed of 1.6 cm per year.

Remember to include a unit in your answer.

a) If the sea level remains the same, how much will the Red Sea widen in 10 000 years?

....

b) The Red Sea is currently exactly 325 km wide at a certain point. If the sea level remains the same, how wide will the Red Sea be at this point in 20 000 years' time?

....

....

Don't forget to make sure your distances are in the same unit.

Q2 The map below on the left shows where most of the world's earthquakes take place.

= main earthquake zones

Compare this map to one showing the tectonic plates.
What do you notice about the main earthquake zones?

....

....

The Earth's Structure

Q3   Draw a simple diagram of the Earth's structure.
Label the crust, mantle and core and write a brief description of each.

Q4   Match up the description to the key phrase or word.

| Crust | | Hot spots that often sit on plate boundaries |

Crust   Hot spots that often sit on plate boundaries

Mantle   Caused by sudden movements of plates

Convection current   Caused by heat from radioactive decay in the mantle

Tectonic plates   Thinnest of the Earth's layers

Earthquakes   Large pieces of crust and upper mantle

Volcanoes   Slowly flowing semi-solid layer that plates float on

Q5   How do scientists predict volcanic eruptions and earthquakes?
Complete the table to show what **evidence** can be collected, and comment on its **reliability**.

	Evidence	How reliable is it?
Earthquake		
Volcanic eruption		

Top Tips: That's the problem with "evidence" predicting earthquakes and volcanic eruptions — it's nowhere near 100% reliable. There are likely to be shed-loads of people living near a volcano or on a fault line — it'd be impossible to evacuate them all every time scientists thought there might possibly be an eruption or an earthquake some time soon — it just wouldn't work.

Chemistry 1b — Oils, Earth and Atmosphere

The Evolution of the Atmosphere

Q1 Tick the boxes to show whether these sentences are **true** or **false**.

              True   False

a) When the Earth was formed, its surface was molten. ☐ ☐

b) The Earth's early atmosphere is thought to have been mostly oxygen. ☐ ☐

c) When plants died and were buried under layers of sediment, the carbon they had removed from the atmosphere became locked up as fossil fuels. ☐ ☐

Q2 The amount of **carbon dioxide** in the atmosphere has changed over the last 4.5 billion or so years.

Describe how the level of carbon dioxide has changed and explain why this change happened.

....

....

....

....

Q3 Draw lines to put the statements in the **right order** on the timeline. One is done for you.

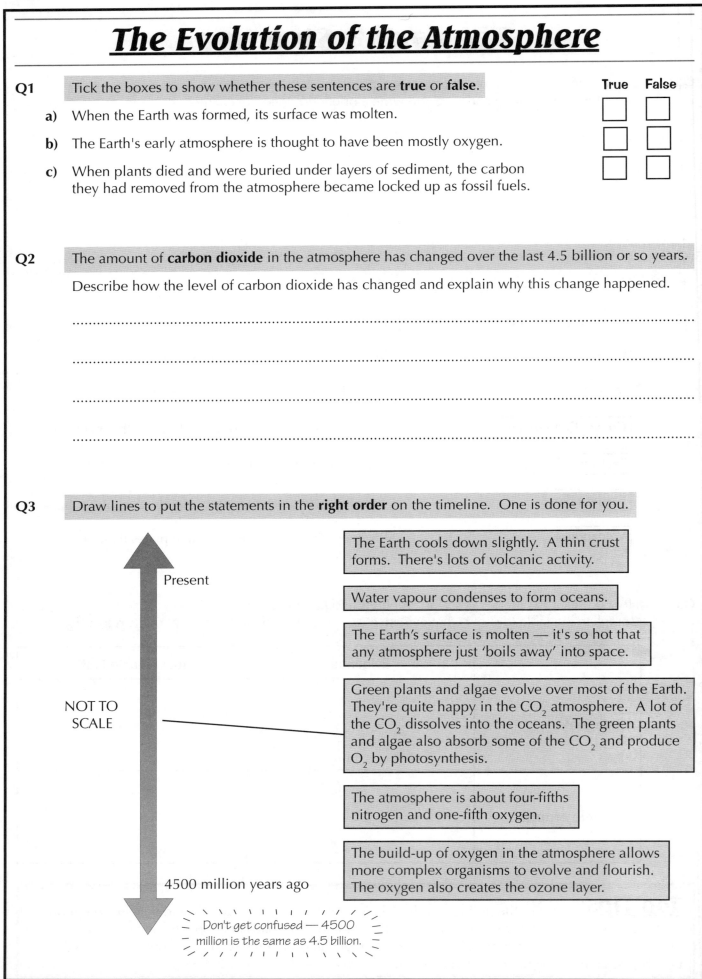

Present

NOT TO SCALE

4500 million years ago

The Earth cools down slightly. A thin crust forms. There's lots of volcanic activity.

Water vapour condenses to form oceans.

The Earth's surface is molten — it's so hot that any atmosphere just 'boils away' into space.

Green plants and algae evolve over most of the Earth. They're quite happy in the CO_2 atmosphere. A lot of the CO_2 dissolves into the oceans. The green plants and algae also absorb some of the CO_2 and produce O_2 by photosynthesis.

The atmosphere is about four-fifths nitrogen and one-fifth oxygen.

The build-up of oxygen in the atmosphere allows more complex organisms to evolve and flourish. The oxygen also creates the ozone layer.

Don't get confused — 4500 million is the same as 4.5 billion.

The Evolution of the Atmosphere

Q4 The pie chart below shows the proportions of different gases in the Earth's atmosphere today.

a) Add the labels '**Nitrogen**', '**Oxygen**', and '**Carbon dioxide and other gases**'.

b) Give the approximate percentages of the following gases in the air today:

Nitrogen ....

Oxygen ....

Earth's Atmosphere Today

Water vapour

c) This pie chart shows the proportions of different gases that we think were in the Earth's atmosphere 4500 million years ago.

Earth's Atmosphere 4500 Million Years Ago

Carbon dioxide

Nitrogen

Other gases

Water vapour

Describe the main differences between today's atmosphere and the atmosphere 4500 million years ago.

....

....

d) Explain why the amount of water vapour has decreased.

....

....

What did the water vapour change into?

e) Explain how oxygen was introduced into the atmosphere.

....

f) What were two effects of the rising oxygen levels in the atmosphere?

1. ....

....

2. ....

....

Life, Resources and Atmospheric Change

Q1   Air is a source of **resources** that can be used in industry.

a)   Put numbers in the boxes to show the order of the stages in the fractional distillation of air.

☐   Air is filtered to remove dust.

☐   Air is cooled to -200 °C.

☐   Liquefied air enters the fractionating column and is heated slowly.

☐   Carbon dioxide freezes and is removed. Water vapour condenses and is removed.

b)   Fill in the gaps with the words below to explain why air can be separated by fractional distillation.

compound	boiling points	vapour	mixture	weights	fractions
Air is a .... of gases with different					

c)   Give two gases used in industry that the fractional distillation of air produces.

....

Q2   There are many theories of how life on Earth was formed.

a)   Briefly describe the '**primordial soup**' theory.

....

....

....

....

b)   Describe the experiment that was carried out by Miller and Urey to try and prove this theory.

....

....

c)   Describe what happened in the experiment. What does this suggests about the theory?

....

....

Life, Resources and Atmospheric Change

Q3 The graphs below show the changes in the atmospheric carbon dioxide level and temperature since 1850.

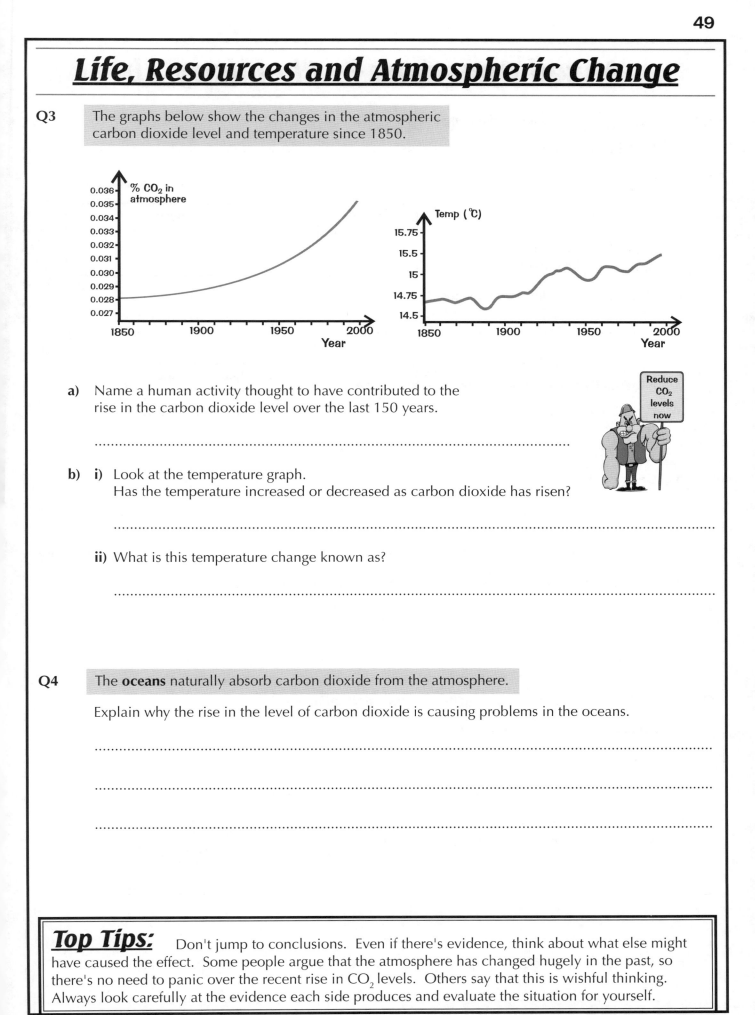

a) Name a human activity thought to have contributed to the rise in the carbon dioxide level over the last 150 years.

....

b) i) Look at the temperature graph.
Has the temperature increased or decreased as carbon dioxide has risen?

....

ii) What is this temperature change known as?

....

Q4 The **oceans** naturally absorb carbon dioxide from the atmosphere.

Explain why the rise in the level of carbon dioxide is causing problems in the oceans.

....

....

....

Top Tips: Don't jump to conclusions. Even if there's evidence, think about what else might have caused the effect. Some people argue that the atmosphere has changed hugely in the past, so there's no need to panic over the recent rise in CO_2 levels. Others say that this is wishful thinking. Always look carefully at the evidence each side produces and evaluate the situation for yourself.

Mixed Questions — Chemistry 1b

Q1 The general formula for an alkene is C_nH_{2n}.

a) **Explain** what this general formula means. ....

....

b) The displayed structure for ethene is shown to the right.
Draw the displayed structure for propene in the other box.

Ethene	Propene
H\C = C/H (with H below each C)	

c) How do alkenes differ from alkanes?

....

Q2 Octane is heated and passed over a catalyst. It **thermally decomposes** as shown to the right.

octane → hexane + ethene

a) What is the process of splitting up long-chain hydrocarbons by thermal decomposition called?

....

b) Describe how ethene can be used to make **ethanol**.

....

....

c) Suggest **one** other way to make ethanol. What is the advantage of making it this way?

....

....

Q3 Ethene molecules can join together in a **polymerisation** reaction.

a) **Explain** the term '**polymerisation**'.

....

....

b) Styrene molecules can also join together to form a polymer.
Name this polymer and **draw** a diagram of part of it below.

Styrene

....

c) **Plastics** are polymers. Most plastics aren't biodegradable. Explain one problem this creates.

....

Chemistry 1b — Oils, Earth and Atmosphere

Mixed Questions — Chemistry 1b

Q4 The **ingredients** list from a tin of **macaroni cheese** is shown below.

> **Macaroni Cheese — Ingredients**
> Water, Durum Wheat, Cheddar Cheese, Rapeseed Oil, Salt,
> Sugar, Skimmed Milk Powder, Mustard, Emulsifiers, Flavour
> Enhancer (E621), Colour (E160)

a) Describe how rapeseed oil is obtained.

....

....

b) Rapeseed oil is an unsaturated oil. Circle the words to complete the sentence below.

Rapeseed oil will / will not turn bromine water from orange to colourless.

c) Cheddar cheese contains a lot of saturated fat.
Name a **health problem** that too much saturated fat can cause. ....

d) The macaroni cheese contains emulsifiers.

  i) What do emulsifiers do?

  ....

  ii) Give **one** advantage and **one** disadvantage of using emulsifiers in foods.

  Advantage ....

  Disadvantage ....

Q5 People used to think that the Earth's surface was all one piece.
Today, we think it's made up of **separate plates** of rock.

a) It wasn't until the 1960s that geologists were convinced that this was the case.
Suggest why there was little evidence to support the theory before the 1960s.

....

....

....

b) What is thought to cause the **movement** of the plates?

....

c) Name **two** kinds of natural disasters that can occur at the boundaries between plates.

.... and ....

Mixed Questions — Chemistry 1b

Q6 The graphs below give information about the Earth's atmosphere millions of years ago and today.

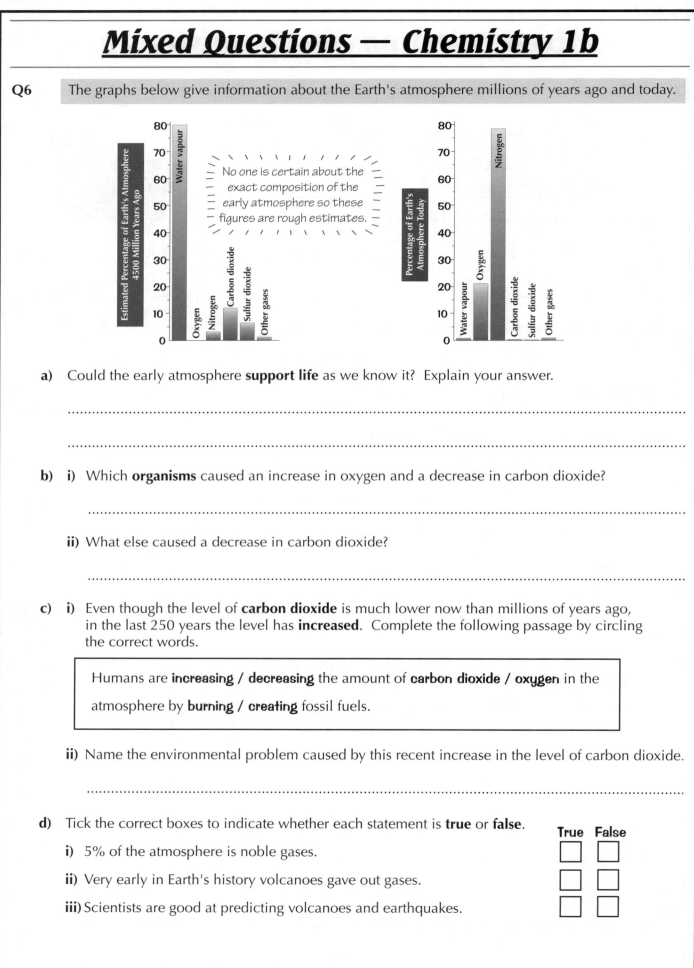

No one is certain about the exact composition of the early atmosphere so these figures are rough estimates.

a) Could the early atmosphere **support life** as we know it? Explain your answer.

....

....

b) i) Which **organisms** caused an increase in oxygen and a decrease in carbon dioxide?

....

ii) What else caused a decrease in carbon dioxide?

....

c) i) Even though the level of **carbon dioxide** is much lower now than millions of years ago, in the last 250 years the level has **increased**. Complete the following passage by circling the correct words.

> Humans are **increasing / decreasing** the amount of **carbon dioxide / oxygen** in the atmosphere by **burning / creating** fossil fuels.

ii) Name the environmental problem caused by this recent increase in the level of carbon dioxide.

....

d) Tick the correct boxes to indicate whether each statement is **true** or **false**.

                                                                       True False

i) 5% of the atmosphere is noble gases.   ☐ ☐

ii) Very early in Earth's history volcanoes gave out gases.   ☐ ☐

iii) Scientists are good at predicting volcanoes and earthquakes.   ☐ ☐

Atoms, Compounds and Isotopes

Q1   **Complete** this table to show the relative masses of the particles in an atom.

Particle	Mass
Proton	1
	1
Electron	

Q2   Elements have a **mass number** and an **atomic number**.

a)   Circle the **mass number** on the diagram to the right.

$$^{12}_{6}\text{C}$$

b)   What does the **mass number** of an element tell you about its atoms?

....

c)   What is the name for a substance that contains two
or more different elements chemically combined?

....

Q3   Choose the correct words from the list to **complete** this paragraph.

electrons	element	isotopes	protons	compound	neutrons

.... are different atomic forms of the same .... which have

the same number of .... but a different number of ....

Q4   Which of the following atoms are **isotopes** of each other? Explain your answer.

W $^{12}_{6}\text{C}$ **X** $^{4}_{2}\text{He}$ **Y** $^{14}_{6}\text{C}$ **Z** $^{14}_{7}\text{N}$

Answer .... and ....

Explanation ....

....

Ionic Bonding

Q1 Tick the boxes to show whether the following statements are **true** or **false**.

True False

a) i) In ionic bonding, atoms lose or gain electrons. ☐ ☐

   ii) Ions with opposite charges attract each other. ☐ ☐

   iii) Atoms form ionic bonds to avoid having the same
      electronic structure as the noble gases. ☐ ☐

   iv) Ionic bonds always produce giant ionic lattices. ☐ ☐

   v) In ionic bonding, electrons from the inner shell are transferred. ☐ ☐

   vi) Ionic compounds dissolve to form solutions that conduct electricity. ☐ ☐

b) Write out corrected versions of any **false** statements.

....

....

....

....

Q2 Magnesium (Group 2) and oxygen (Group 6) react to form **magnesium oxide**.

a) How many electrons does magnesium need to **lose** to get a full outer shell? ....

b) How many electrons does oxygen need to **gain** to get a full outer shell? ....

Q3 Sodium chloride (salt) has a **giant ionic structure**.

a) Circle the correct words from each pair to explain why sodium chloride has a **high melting point**.

> Sodium chloride has very **strong** / **weak** electrostatic forces of attraction
> between the **negative** / **positive** sodium ions and the **negative** / **positive**
> chlorine ions. These forces act in **one direction** / **all directions**.
> This means that it needs a **little** / **large** amount of energy to break the bonds.

b) Name two other **properties** of compounds with **giant ionic structures**.

1. ....

2. ....

Ionic Bonding

Q4 Diagrams can be used to represent the **structure** of chemical substances.

a) Tick the correct box to show which of the following diagrams could be used to represent the bonding in **sodium chloride**.

i)

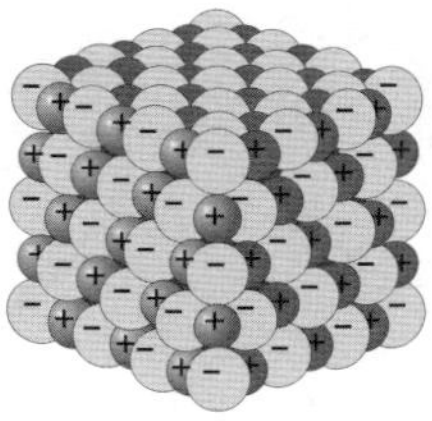

ii)

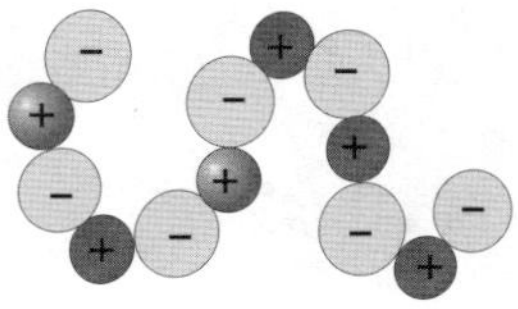

iii)

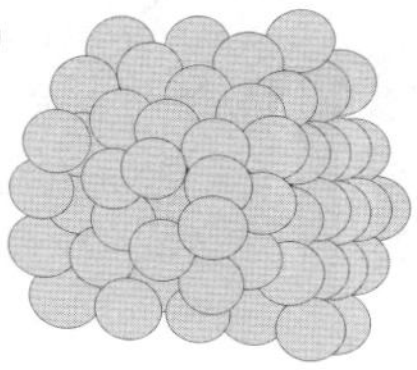

□ □ □

b) Explain your answer to **a)**.

....

....

....

Q5 Mike conducts an experiment to find out if an **ionic compound** conducts electricity. He tests the compound when it's solid, when it's dissolved in water and when it's molten.

a) Complete the following table of results.

	Conducts electricity?
When solid	
When dissolved in water	
When molten	

b) Explain your answers to part **a)**.

....

....

....

....

Top Tips: Giant ionic structures are the first of four different types of structure that you need to know about. You'll have to be able to identify the structure in different compounds later on — so make sure you can describe and recognise their properties now.

Ions and Formulas

Q1   Use the **diagram** to help you answer the following questions.

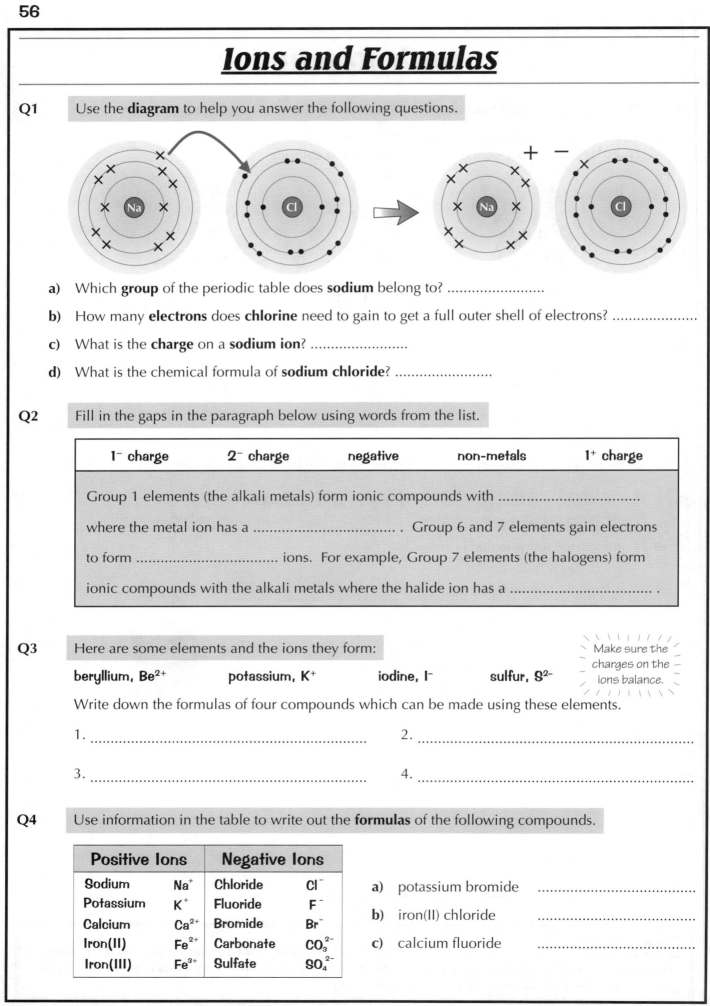

a)   Which **group** of the periodic table does **sodium** belong to? ....

b)   How many **electrons** does **chlorine** need to gain to get a full outer shell of electrons? ....

c)   What is the **charge** on a **sodium ion**? ....

d)   What is the chemical formula of **sodium chloride**? ....

Q2   Fill in the gaps in the paragraph below using words from the list.

1⁻ charge	2⁻ charge	negative	non-metals	1⁺ charge

Group 1 elements (the alkali metals) form ionic compounds with ....

where the metal ion has a .... Group 6 and 7 elements gain electrons

to form .... ions. For example, Group 7 elements (the halogens) form

ionic compounds with the alkali metals where the halide ion has a ....

Q3   Here are some elements and the ions they form:

Make sure the charges on the ions balance.

beryllium, Be^{2+} potassium, K^+ iodine, I^- sulfur, S^{2-}

Write down the formulas of four compounds which can be made using these elements.

1. ....

2. ....

3. ....

4. ....

Q4   Use information in the table to write out the **formulas** of the following compounds.

Positive Ions		Negative Ions	
Sodium	Na^+	Chloride	Cl^-
Potassium	K^+	Fluoride	F^-
Calcium	Ca^{2+}	Bromide	Br^-
Iron(II)	Fe^{2+}	Carbonate	CO_3^{2-}
Iron(III)	Fe^{3+}	Sulfate	SO_4^{2-}

a)   potassium bromide   ....

b)   iron(II) chloride   ....

c)   calcium fluoride   ....

Chemistry 2a — Bonding and Calculations

Electronic Structure of Ions

Q1 Complete these diagrams to show the **electronic structure** and **charge** of the following ions. (The first one's been done for you.)

You can use the periodic table in the front of this book to help you.

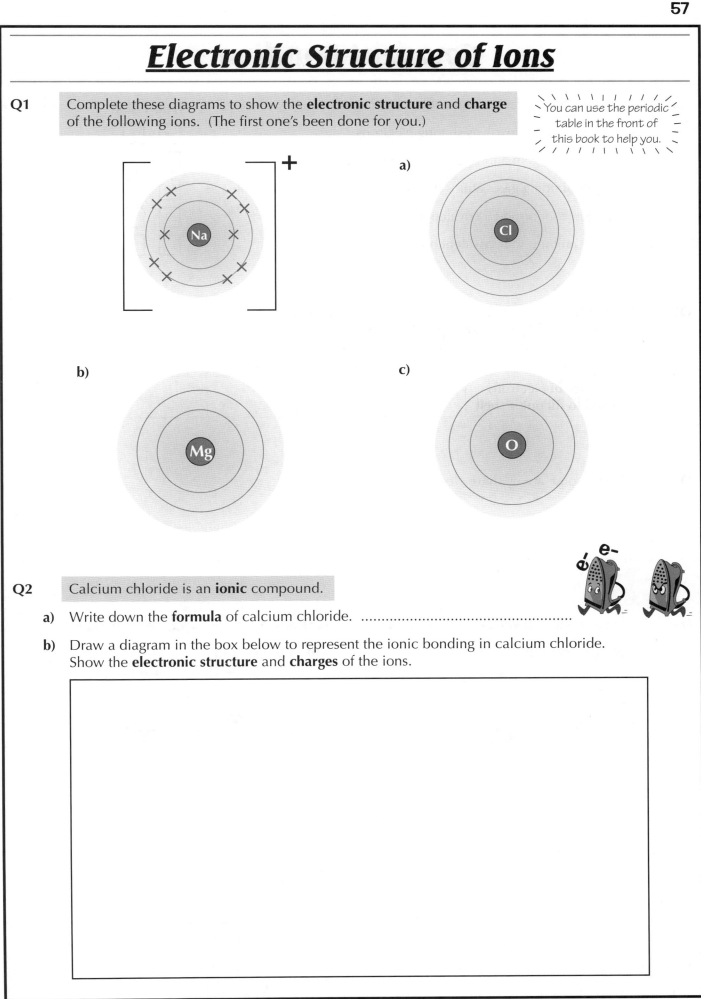

a)

b)

c)

Q2 Calcium chloride is an **ionic** compound.

a) Write down the **formula** of calcium chloride. ....

b) Draw a diagram in the box below to represent the ionic bonding in calcium chloride. Show the **electronic structure** and **charges** of the ions.

Covalent Bonding

Q1   Indicate whether each statement is **true** or **false**.

		True	False
a)	Covalent bonding involves sharing electrons.	☐	☐
b)	Atoms react to gain a full outer shell of electrons.	☐	☐
c)	Covalent bonding gives atoms the electronic structure of a noble gas.	☐	☐
d)	Hydrogen can form two covalent bonds.	☐	☐
e)	Carbon can form four covalent bonds.	☐	☐

Q2   **Complete** the following table to show how many electrons are needed to **fill up** the **outer shell** of these atoms.

You can use a periodic table to help you with this.

Atom	Carbon	Chlorine	Hydrogen	Nitrogen	Oxygen
Number of electrons needed to fill outer shell					

Q3   Why do some atoms **share** electrons?

....

....

Q4   Complete the following diagrams by adding the **electrons**. Only the outer shells are shown.

a) Hydrogen chloride (HCl)

b) Oxygen (O_2)

c) Water (H_2O)

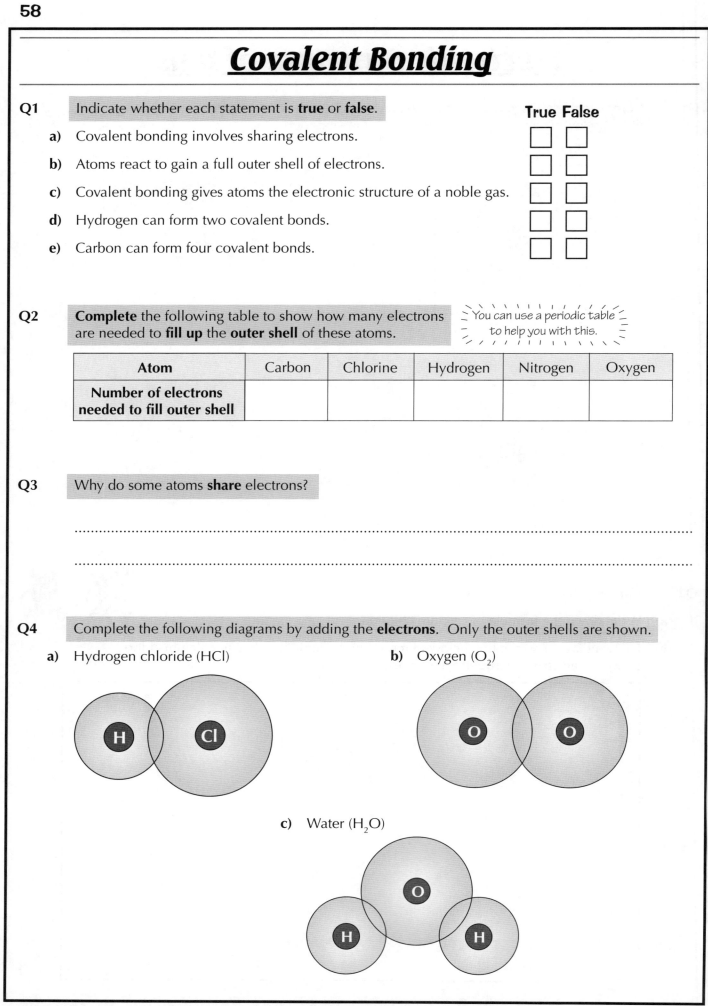

Covalent Bonding

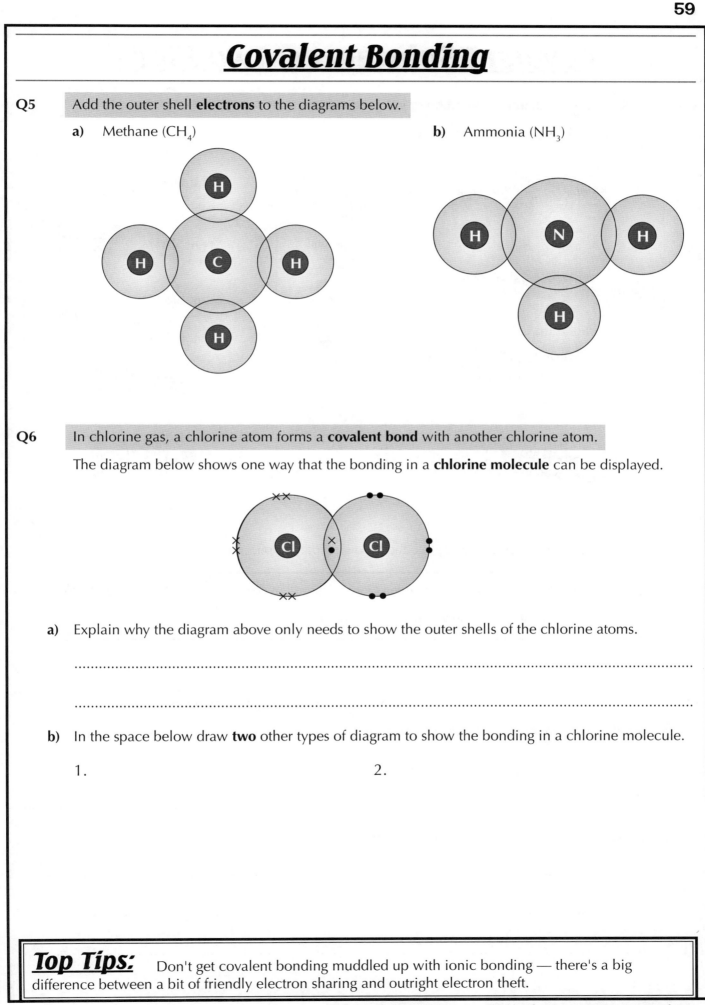

Q5 Add the outer shell **electrons** to the diagrams below.

a) Methane (CH$_4$)

b) Ammonia (NH$_3$)

Q6 In chlorine gas, a chlorine atom forms a **covalent bond** with another chlorine atom.

The diagram below shows one way that the bonding in a **chlorine molecule** can be displayed.

a) Explain why the diagram above only needs to show the outer shells of the chlorine atoms.

....

....

b) In the space below draw **two** other types of diagram to show the bonding in a chlorine molecule.

1.   2.

Top Tips: Don't get covalent bonding muddled up with ionic bonding — there's a big difference between a bit of friendly electron sharing and outright electron theft.

Covalent Substances: Two Kinds

Q1 Which am I — **diamond**, **graphite** or **silicon dioxide**?

Match up the statements to the drawings below.

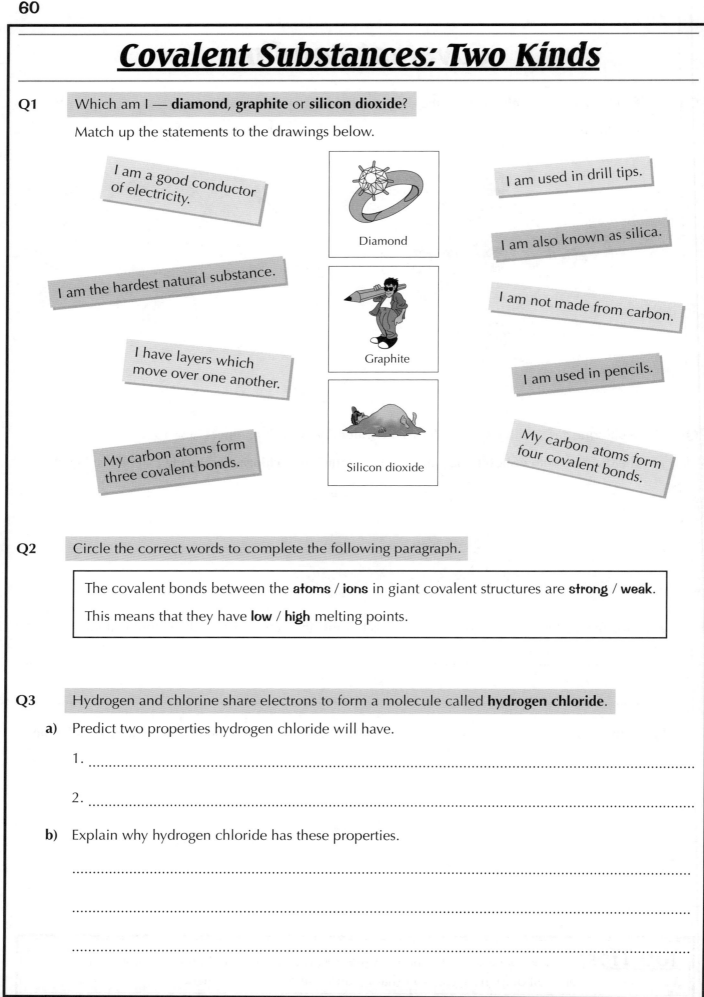

I am a good conductor of electricity.

I am used in drill tips.

I am also known as silica.

I am the hardest natural substance.

I am not made from carbon.

I have layers which move over one another.

I am used in pencils.

My carbon atoms form three covalent bonds.

My carbon atoms form four covalent bonds.

Diamond

Graphite

Silicon dioxide

Q2 Circle the correct words to complete the following paragraph.

The covalent bonds between the **atoms** / **ions** in giant covalent structures are **strong** / **weak**.

This means that they have **low** / **high** melting points.

Q3 Hydrogen and chlorine share electrons to form a molecule called **hydrogen chloride**.

a) Predict two properties hydrogen chloride will have.

1. ....

2. ....

b) Explain why hydrogen chloride has these properties.

....

....

....

Covalent Substances: Two Kinds

Q4   There are two types of **covalent substance**.

a) Name the **two** types of covalent substance.

1. ....

2. ....

b) Draw lines to match the following **covalent substances** to the diagrams.

| Graphite | Diamond | Silicon dioxide |

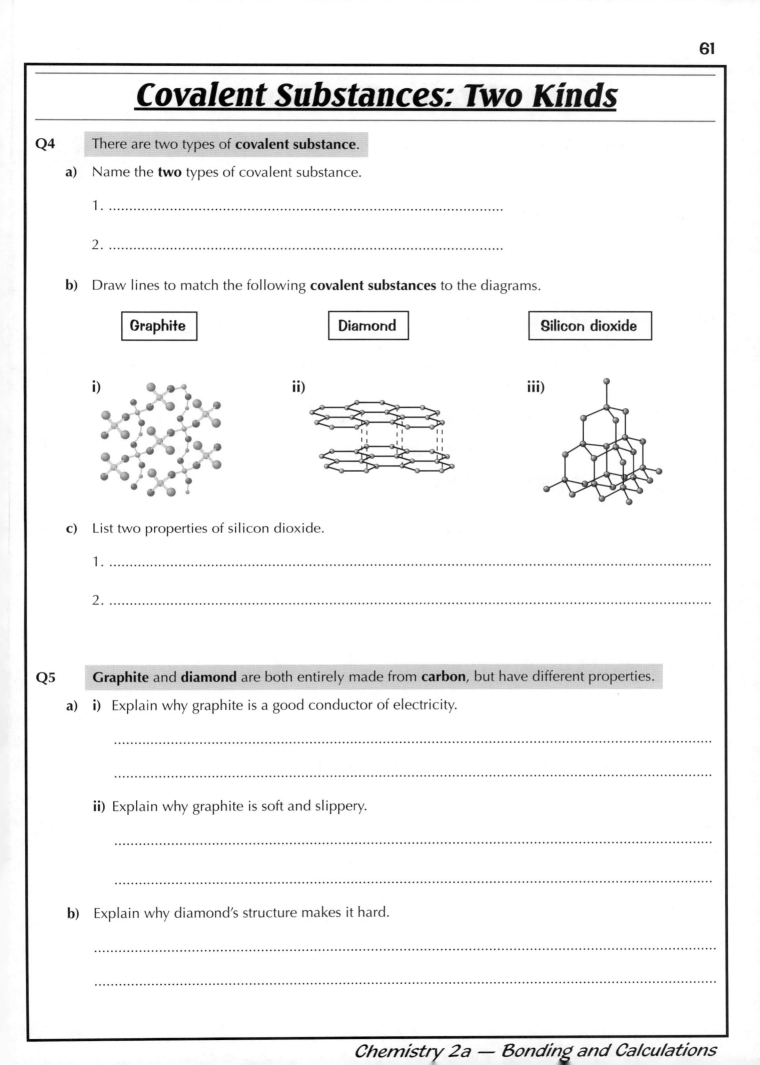

i)   ii)   iii)

c) List two properties of silicon dioxide.

1. ....

2. ....

Q5   **Graphite** and **diamond** are both entirely made from **carbon**, but have different properties.

a) i) Explain why graphite is a good conductor of electricity.

....

....

ii) Explain why graphite is soft and slippery.

....

....

b) Explain why diamond's structure makes it hard.

....

....

Metallic Structures

Q1   **Complete** the following sentences about metals.

a)   Metals have a .... metallic structure.

b)   Metals are good conductors of .... and electricity.

c)   The .... in metals can slide over each other, so metals can be bent.

Q2   Metals consist of a **giant structure**.

a)   Circle the correct words from each pair in the passage below.

> Every metal atom in the structure provides one or more free **electrons** / **ions**
>
> from its **outer** / **inner** shell. There are **strong** / **weak** forces of electrostatic attraction
>
> between these and the **positive** / **negative** metal ions. This holds the metals atoms
>
> together in **a regular** / **an irregular** structure.

b)   How do metals **conduct electricity**?

....

....

Q3   Copper is a **pure metal**. Brass is an **alloy**.

a)   What is an alloy?

....

b)   Explain how the structures of copper and brass relate to how hard they are.

....

....

....

....

....

....

Metallic Structures

Q4 What type of **structure** is present in substances which:

Choose from giant ionic, giant covalent, simple molecular or giant metallic.

a) Don't conduct electricity when solid, but do when liquid. ....

b) Have high melting points and don't conduct electricity when molten. ....

c) Conduct electricity when solid and liquid. ....

Q5 Complete the following table by placing a **tick** or a **cross** in each box.

Property	Giant Ionic	Giant Covalent	Simple Molecular	Giant Metallic
High melting and boiling points				
Can conduct electricity when solid		except graphite		
Can conduct electricity when molten		except graphite		

Q6 The **properties** of four substances are given below.

Substance	Melting Point (°C)	Good Electrical Conductor?
A	2000	Only when molten or dissolved
B	2500	No
C	20	No
D	600	Yes

Identify the **structure** of each substance. Explain your choice.

a) Substance A ....

....

b) Substance B ....

....

c) Substance C ....

....

d) Substance D ....

....

New Materials

Q1   **Nitinol** is a smart material.

   a) True or false?

          True False

     i) Nitinol is a mixture of metals.   ☐ ☐

     ii) Nitinol is affected by light.   ☐ ☐

     iii) When cool, nitinol can bend and twist like rubber.   ☐ ☐

   b) Write out corrected versions of any **false** statements.

....

....

   c) Explain why nitinol is sometimes called a 'shape memory alloy'.

....

....

   d) Give one use of nitinol.

....

Q2   **Nanoparticles** are a new type of material.

   a) Circle the correct words from each pair in the sentences below.

> Nanoparticles contain roughly a few **hundred** / **thousand** atoms.
>
> Nanoparticles have **identical** / **different** properties to the bulk material they are made from.

   b) Explain why nanoparticles could help make new industrial **catalysts**.

....

....

Q3   Nanoparticles are really tiny particles, between 1 and 100 nanometres across.

How many nanometres are there in **1 mm**?

....

1 nm = 0.000 001 mm

....

Chemistry 2a — Bonding and Calculations

New Materials

Q4 There are different types of **nanoparticles**.

a) Choose from the words below to complete the paragraph.

molecules	shape memory alloys	atoms	fullerenes	hexagonal

Nanoparticles include .... These are ....

made from carbon atoms. The atoms are arranged in .... rings.

Different fullerenes contain different numbers of carbon ....

b) The **properties** of nanoparticles determine their use. Draw lines to match the properties and uses.

Lightweight but strong

Can detect specific molecules

Act like ball bearings to reduce friction

Lubricants for artificial joints

Building materials

Sensors to test water purity

c) What is the study of nanoparticles known as? Circle the correct word from the list below.

particle science   nanoscience   nanotubes   smart materials

d) Fullerenes are being developed for use in **medicine**.
They could be used to deliver **drugs** right into the cells where they are needed in the body.
Suggest what **property** fullerenes have that makes them suitable for this use.

....

....

Q5 Fullerenes can be joined together to make **nanotubes**.

a) Give a property of nanotubes that makes them useful as **electrical circuits** in computers.

....

b) Explain why nanotubes are often used to reinforce the graphite used to make **tennis rackets**.

....

....

Top Tips: Your old friend the examiner might ask you to evaluate the development and use of new materials. So, on the upside you can talk about how you can make weird and wonderful things with them. Then on the downside you can talk about the fact that, because they're so new, they could also have strange, scary properties that we haven't had time to find out about yet.

Polymers

Q1 **Polymer** molecules are **long chains**, as shown in the diagrams.

A

B

a) Which diagram shows a **thermosoftening** polymer? ....

b) Explain why **thermosetting** polymers don't melt when heated.

....

....

Q2 There are many different types of **polymers**.

Different polymers have different properties.
Give two factors that affect the properties of a polymer when it's made.

1. ....

2. ....

Q3 **High density polythene** and **low density polythene** have different properties.

The table compares some of their properties.

	DENSITY	SOFTENING TEMP.	FLEXIBILITY
LDP	Low	Below 100 °C	High
HDP	High	Above 100 °C	Fairly low

For each of the following applications choose which type of polythene should be used
and give a reason for your choice.

a) toothpaste tubes ....

....

b) freezer bags ....

....

c) hospital equipment that has to be sterilised ....

....

Relative Formula Mass

Q1 a) What is meant by the **relative atomic mass** of an element?

....

b) What are the **relative atomic masses (A$_r$)** of the following:

i) magnesium ....   **iv)** hydrogen ....   **vii)** K ....

ii) neon ....   **v)** C ....   **viii)** Ca ....

iii) oxygen ....   **vi)** Cu ....   **ix)** Cl ....

Q2 Use a periodic table to help identify the elements A, B and C.

> Element A has an A$_r$ of 4.
> Element B has an A$_r$ 3 times that of element A.
> Element C has an A$_r$ 4 times that of element A.

Element A is ....   Element B is ....

Element C is ....

Q3 a) Explain how the **relative formula mass** of a **compound** is calculated.

....

b) What are the **relative formula masses (M$_r$)** of the following:

i) water (H_2O) ....

ii) potassium hydroxide (KOH) ....

iii) nitric acid (HNO_3) ....

iv) sulfuric acid (H_2SO_4) ....

v) ammonium nitrate (NH_4NO_3) ....

Q4 The equation below shows a reaction between element X and water. The total M$_r$ of the products is **114**. What is substance X?

$$2X + 2H_2O \rightarrow 2XOH + H_2$$

....

....

Top Tips: The periodic table really comes in useful here. There's no way you'll be able to answer these questions without one (unless you've memorised all the elements' relative atomic masses — and that would just be silly). And lucky for you, you'll get given one in your exam. Yay!

Chemistry 2a — Bonding and Calculations

Two Formula Mass Calculations

Q1 a) Write down the **formula** for calculating the **percentage mass** of an element in a compound.

b) Calculate the percentage mass of the following elements in ammonium nitrate, NH_4NO_3.

i) Nitrogen ....

ii) Hydrogen ....

iii) Oxygen ....

Q2 a) Calculate the percentage mass of **oxygen** in each of the following compounds.

A Fe_2O_3 **B** H_2O **C** $CaCO_3$

b) Which compound has the **greatest** percentage mass of oxygen? ....

Q3 **Nitrogen monoxide**, NO, reacts with oxygen, O_2, to form **oxide R**.

a) Calculate the percentage mass of nitrogen in **nitrogen monoxide**.

....

b) Oxide R has a percentage composition by mass of **30.4% nitrogen** and **69.6% oxygen**. Work out its empirical formula.

....

....

Q4 1.48 g of a **calcium compound** contains 0.8 g of calcium, 0.64 g of oxygen and 0.04 g of hydrogen.

Work out the empirical formula of the compound.

....

....

69

Calculating Masses in Reactions

Q1 | Anna burns **10 g** of **magnesium** in air to produce **magnesium oxide** (MgO).

a) Write out the **balanced equation** for this reaction.

....

b) Calculate the mass of **magnesium oxide** that's produced.

....

....

....

Q2 | What mass of **sodium** is needed to make **2 g** of **sodium oxide**?

Balanced Equation:

$$4Na + O_2 \rightarrow 2Na_2O$$

....

....

....

Q3 | **Aluminium** and **iron oxide** (Fe_2O_3) react together to produce **aluminium oxide** (Al_2O_3) and **iron**.

a) Write out the **balanced equation** for this reaction.

....

b) What **mass** of iron is produced from **20 g** of iron oxide?

....

....

....

Q4 | When heated, **limestone** ($CaCO_3$) decomposes to form **calcium oxide** (CaO) and **carbon dioxide**.

How many **kilograms** of limestone are needed to make **100 kilograms** of **calcium oxide**?

The calculation is exactly the same — just use 'kg' instead of 'g'.

....

....

....

Calculating Masses in Reactions

Q5 Iron oxide is reduced to iron inside a blast furnace using carbon. There are three stages involved.

> Stage A $C + O_2 \rightarrow CO_2$
>
> Stage B $CO_2 + C \rightarrow 2CO$
>
> Stage C $3CO + Fe_2O_3 \rightarrow 2Fe + 3CO_2$

a) If **10 g** of **carbon** are used in stage B, and all the carbon monoxide produced gets used in stage C, what **mass** of CO_2 is produced in **stage C**?

....

....

....

....

Work out the mass of CO at the end of stage B first.

b) Suggest how the CO_2 might be used after stage C.

....

Look at where CO_2 is used.

Q6 **Sodium sulfate** (Na_2SO_4) is made by reacting **sodium hydroxide** (NaOH) with **sulfuric acid** (H_2SO_4). **Water** is also produced.

a) Write out the **balanced equation** for this reaction.

....

b) What mass of **sodium hydroxide** is needed to make **75 g** of **sodium sulfate**?

....

....

....

....

c) What mass of **water** is formed when **50 g** of **sulfuric acid** reacts?

....

....

....

....

Percentage Yield and Reversible Reactions

Q1 Aaliya and Natasha mixed together barium chloride ($BaCl_2$) and sodium sulfate (Na_2SO_4) solutions in a beaker. **Insoluble** barium sulfate was formed. They **filtered** the solution to obtain the solid substance, and then transferred the solid to a clean piece of **filter paper** and left it to dry.

a) Complete the following paragraph using the words provided.

percentage yield	lost	yield	lower	predicted	higher

The amount of product you get from a reaction is known as the ....

The more reactants you start with, the .... it will be.

The .... compares how much product you actually get to the

amount you ....

b) Aaliya calculated that they should produce a yield of **15 g** of barium sulfate. However, after completing the experiment they found they had only obtained **6 g**.

Calculate the **percentage yield** for this reaction.

....

....

c) Suggest **one** reason why their actual yield was lower than their predicted yield.

....

....

d) Explain how the following factors affect the percentage yield.

i) Reversible reactions ....

....

ii) Unexpected reactions ....

....

Q2 COP Chemicals makes **substance X** using a process that has a percentage yield of just **20%**.

The director of COP Chemicals doesn't think the **low percentage yield** is a problem because he is running his business at a **large profit**. Suggest a reason why he should still try to **increase** the percentage yield of substance X.

....

....

Top Tips: Remember that a 100% yield simply doesn't happen in the big bad real world — your yield will always be somewhere between 0 and 100%. It's your job to remember why.

72

Chemical Analysis and Instrumental Methods

Q1 John did a **paper chromatography** experiment on sweet colourings. His results are shown below.

a) Write a brief method for this experiment, describing what John would have done.

....

....

....

....

....

Colour of Sweet	Distance Travelled by Dyes (mm)		
Brown	10	17	18
Red	18		
Green	10	17	
Orange	10	18	26
Blue	5	17	

b) How many dyes do the results indicate that the blue sweet contains? ....

c) Which sweet might contain the same mix of dyes as the red and green sweets together? Give a reason for your answer.

....

Q2 Forensic scientists use **instrumental methods** to analyse substances found at crime scenes.

a) Suspects in criminal cases can only be held for a short period of time without being charged. Suggest why instrumental methods are useful in these circumstances.

....

b) Give **two** other advantages of using instrumental methods.

1. ....

2. ....

Q3 Bob uses **gas chromatography** to separate a sample of a mixture of compounds.

a) The graph on the right is a **chromatograph** of his sample.

i) How many compounds are in the sample? ....

ii) Write down the **retention times** of the compounds.

....

b) What would linking the gas chromatography column to a **mass spectrometer** allow Bob to do?

....

....

Chemistry 2a — Bonding and Calculations

Mixed Questions — Chemistry 2a

Q1 Three forms of the element **carbon** are shown in the diagrams below.

Key:
● carbon atoms

R   S   T

a) **i)** **R** and **S** have the same type of structure. Write down the name of this type of structure.

....

ii) Explain why forms **R** and **S** have very high melting points.

....

....

b) **i)** Which of the above structures would you expect to be **less than 100 nanometers** across?

....

ii) What type of substance is this form of carbon?

....

Q2 Orwell found that 1.4 g of silicon reacted with 7.1 g of chlorine to produce the reactive liquid silicon chloride.

a) Work out the **empirical formula** of the silicon chloride.

....

....

b) Calculate the **percentage mass** of chlorine in silicon chloride.

....

....

c) Write down the balanced chemical equation for the reaction.

....

d) What mass of silicon chloride is produced when 1.4 g of silicon reacts with chlorine?

....

....

Mixed Questions — Chemistry 2a

Q3 The table gives data for some physical **properties** of a selection of elements and compounds.

substance	state at room temp	melting point /°C	boiling point /°C	electrical conductivity	
				solid	liquid
A	solid	114	184	poor	poor
B	gas	-73	-10	poor	poor
C	solid	3550	4827	poor	poor
D	solid	858	1505	poor	good
E	solid	1495	2870	good	good
F	liquid	0	50	poor	poor

a) Identify one substance that is **likely** to have a **simple molecular** structure. Justify your answer.

....

....

b) Which of the substances is **most likely** to have a **giant covalent** structure? ....

c) Explain why substance D is **unlikely** to be a **metallic** element.

....

Q4 There are different types of **polymers**.

Tick the boxes to show whether the following statements are true or false.

True False

a) Thermosoftening polymers have crosslinks. ☐ ☐

b) Thermosetting polymers consist of individual tangled chains of polymers. ☐ ☐

c) Thermosetting polymers don't soften when heated. ☐ ☐

Q5 **Magnesium** reacts with **nitric acid** (HNO_3) to form **magnesium nitrate** ($Mg(NO_3)_2$).

a) Work out the **relative formula mass** of magnesium nitrate.

....

b) The **mass of product** you expect to get in a reaction is known as the **predicted yield**. 12 g of magnesium is reacted with an excess of nitric acid. Work out the **predicted yield** of $Mg(NO_3)_2$.

....

....

c) In real life the **actual yield** is always less than the predicted yield. Give **one** reason why.

....

Mixed Questions — Chemistry 2a

Q6 Different types of substances have different **structures**.

a) Draw lines to match the diagrams below to the type of substance.

i)

ii)

iii)

| Metal | | Ionic Compound | | Alloy |

b) **i)** Which of the above substances would **not conduct electricity** when solid?

....

ii) Explain your answer.

....

....

c) The ionic compound contains Ca^{2+} ions and Cl^- ions. Work out its **formula**.

....

Q7 **Gas chromatography** is a type of instrumental analysis.

a) Use the words below to fill in the gaps in this paragraph about gas chromatography.

> retention time   gas   identify   speeds   chromatograph   compounds   mass spectrometer

A .... is used to carry substances through a column packed with a solid.

The substances travel through it at different ...., so they're separated.

The recorder draws a gas .... The number of peaks shows the number of

different .... in the sample. The position of the peaks shows the

.... of the substances. This helps to .... the substances.

The gas chromatography column can also be linked to a ....

b) Some substances can also be identified using paper chromatography.
Give an **advantage** of using **gas chromatography** instead.

....

Rate of Reaction

Q1   The four statements below are about **rate of reaction**.
Circle the correct words from each pair to complete the sentences.

a)   The **higher** / **lower** the temperature the faster the rate of reaction.

b)   A **higher** / **lower** concentration or pressure will reduce the rate of reaction.

c)   A smaller surface area **increases** / **decreases** the rate of reaction.

d)   A catalyst **does** / **doesn't** change the rate of reaction.

Q2   In an experiment, **different sizes** of marble chips were reacted with excess hydrochloric acid. The **same mass** of marble was used each time. The graph below shows how much **gas** was produced with large marble chips (X), medium marble chips (Y) and small marble chips (Z).

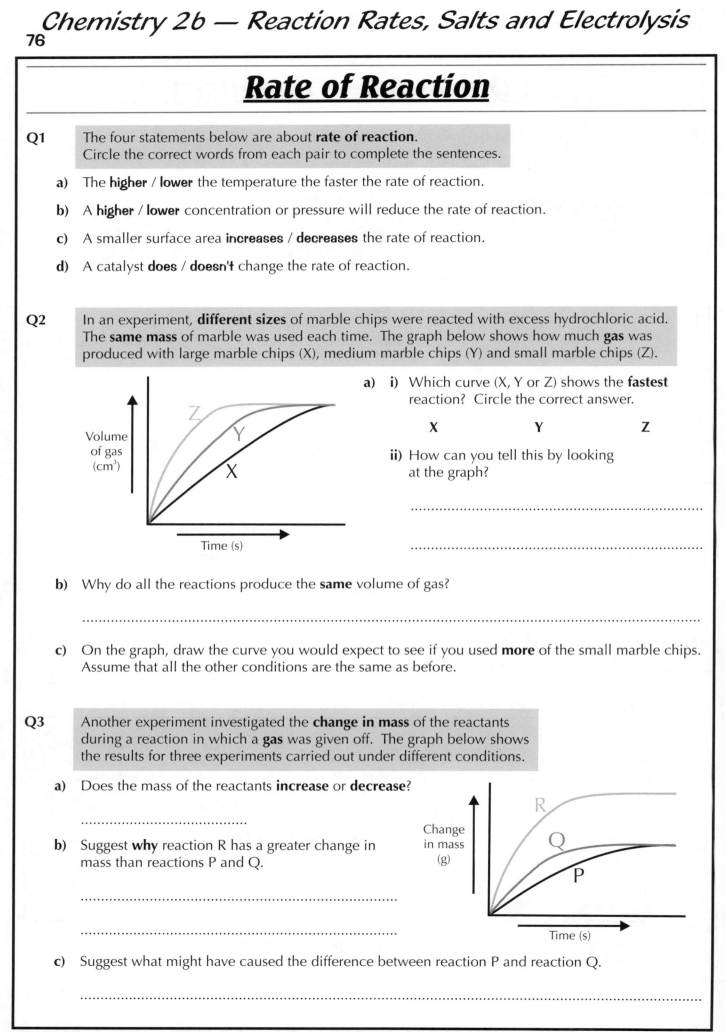

a)   i) Which curve (X, Y or Z) shows the **fastest** reaction? Circle the correct answer.

X   Y   Z

ii) How can you tell this by looking at the graph?

....

....

b)   Why do all the reactions produce the **same** volume of gas?

....

c)   On the graph, draw the curve you would expect to see if you used **more** of the small marble chips. Assume that all the other conditions are the same as before.

Q3   Another experiment investigated the **change in mass** of the reactants during a reaction in which a **gas** was given off. The graph below shows the results for three experiments carried out under different conditions.

a)   Does the mass of the reactants **increase** or **decrease**?

....

b)   Suggest **why** reaction R has a greater change in mass than reactions P and Q.

....

....

c)   Suggest what might have caused the difference between reaction P and reaction Q.

....

Measuring Rates of Reaction

Q1 Use the words provided to complete the sentences below about measuring rates of reaction.

faster	rate	volume	reactants	gas	mass	formed	precipitation

The .... of a reaction can be measured by observing either how quickly

the .... are used up or how quickly the products are ....

In a .... reaction you usually measure how quickly the product is formed.
The product turns the solution cloudy. The .... it turns cloudy the quicker

the reaction.

In a reaction that produces a .... you can measure how quickly the

.... of the reactants changes or measure the .... of

gas given off in a certain time interval.

Q2 Sam conducted an experiment with equal masses of marble chips and equal volumes of hydrochloric acid (HCl). He used two **different concentrations** of acid and measured the **change in mass** of the reactants. Below is a graph of the results.

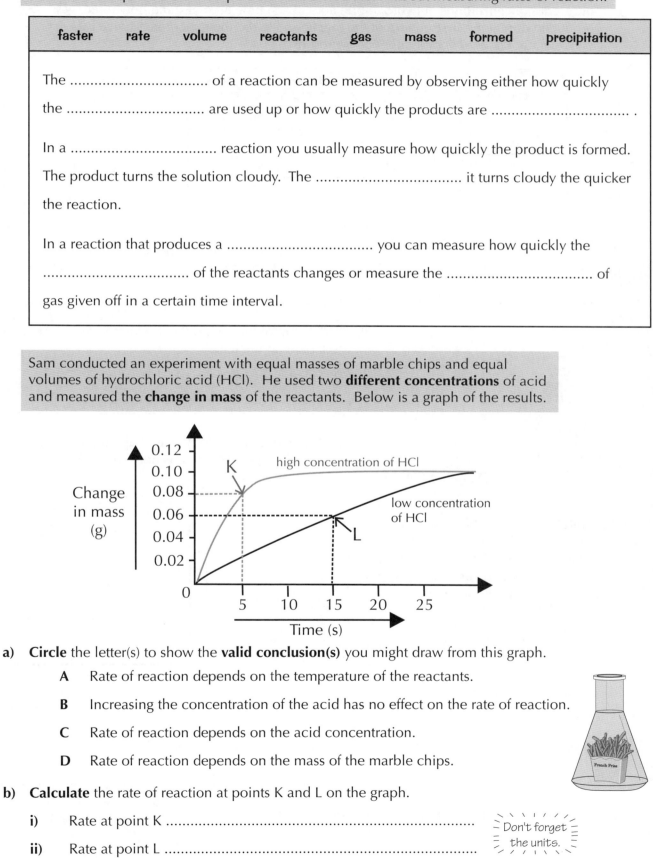

a) **Circle** the letter(s) to show the **valid conclusion(s)** you might draw from this graph.

A   Rate of reaction depends on the temperature of the reactants.

B   Increasing the concentration of the acid has no effect on the rate of reaction.

C   Rate of reaction depends on the acid concentration.

D   Rate of reaction depends on the mass of the marble chips.

b) **Calculate** the rate of reaction at points K and L on the graph.

i)   Rate at point K ....

ii)   Rate at point L ....

Don't forget the units.

Measuring Rates of Reaction

Q3   Charlie was comparing the rate of reaction of 5 g of magnesium ribbon with 20 ml of **five different concentrations** of hydrochloric acid. Each time he measured how much **gas** was produced during the **first minute** of the reaction. He did the experiment **twice** for each concentration of acid and obtained these results:

Concentration of HCl (mol/dm³)	Experiment 1 — volume of gas produced (cm³)	Experiment 2 — volume of gas produced (cm³)	Average volume of gas produced (cm³)
2	92	96	
1.5	63	65	
1	44	47	
0.5	20	50	
0.25	9	9	

a)   **Fill in** the last column of the table.

b)   Circle the **anomalous** result in the table.

> The anomalous result is the one that doesn't seem to fit in.

c)   Which concentration of hydrochloric acid produced the fastest rate of reaction? ....

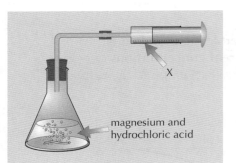

magnesium and hydrochloric acid

d)   A diagram of the **apparatus** used in the experiment is shown on the left.

   i) What is the object marked **X** called?

   ....

   ii) Name one other key piece of apparatus needed for this experiment that is not shown in the diagram.

   ....

e)   **Sketch** a graph of the average volume of gas produced from this investigation against concentration of HCl and **label** the axes. Do not include the anomalous result.

> You don't need to plot the values, just draw what the graph would look like.

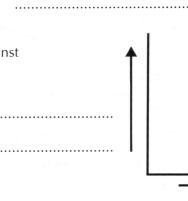

....

....

....

f)   Why did Charlie do the experiment twice and calculate the average volume?

....

g)   How might the **anomalous** result have come about?

....

Rate of Reaction Experiments

Q1   Choose from the words below to complete the paragraph.

smaller	larger	slower	react	decrease	faster	increase

When you crush up a large solid into powder, you .... its surface area.

This means it reacts .... Large lumps have a

.... surface area so they .... more slowly.

Q2   Matilda conducted an experiment to investigate the effect of **surface area** on rate of reaction.
She added dilute hydrochloric acid to **large marble chips** and measured the volume of gas
produced at regular time intervals. She repeated the experiment using the same mass of
powdered marble. Below is a graph of her results.

a)   Which curve, A or B, was
obtained when **large pieces**
of marble were used?

....

b)   On the graph opposite, draw
the curve you would get if you
used the **same mass** of **medium**
sized marble pieces. Label it C.

c)   Name the **independent** variable in this investigation.

....

d)   Is there enough information given above for you to be sure whether this was a **fair test** or not?
Explain your answer.

....

....

....

e)   Which other method(s) could you use to measure the rate of this reaction?
Tick the correct one(s).

☐ Timing how long the reaction takes to go cloudy.

☐ Timing how long the reaction takes to start.

☐ Measuring how quickly the reaction loses mass.

Rate of Reaction Experiments

Q3 Dillon investigated the reaction between **magnesium** and excess **hydrochloric acid**. He did the experiment using **different concentrations** of acid. He recorded the mass of the reactants at the start and at every 10 seconds for 2 minutes and calculated the change in mass for each reading.

a) How many readings did he take for each concentration? ....

b) Suggest the labels (including units) that he might use for a graph of his results:

x-axis ....

y-axis ....

c) On the axes to the right, draw and label sketches of the curves you would expect for a **high** and a **low** concentration of acid.

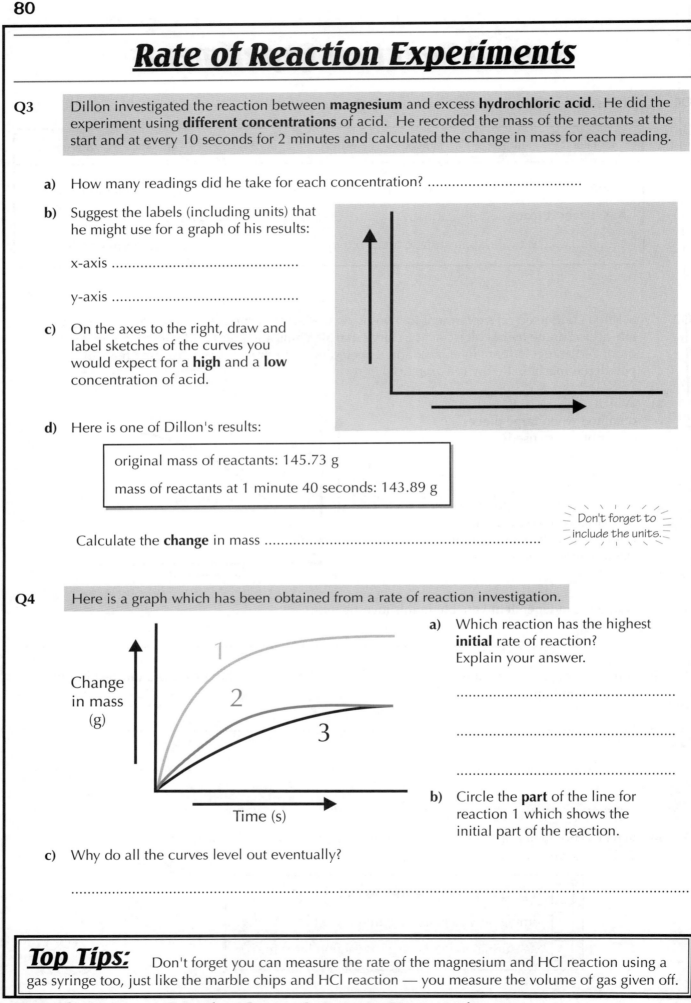

d) Here is one of Dillon's results:

> original mass of reactants: 145.73 g
>
> mass of reactants at 1 minute 40 seconds: 143.89 g

Don't forget to include the units.

Calculate the **change** in mass ....

Q4 Here is a graph which has been obtained from a rate of reaction investigation.

Change in mass (g)

1
2
3

Time (s)

a) Which reaction has the highest **initial** rate of reaction? Explain your answer.

....

....

....

b) Circle the **part** of the line for reaction 1 which shows the initial part of the reaction.

c) Why do all the curves level out eventually?

....

Top Tips: Don't forget you can measure the rate of the magnesium and HCl reaction using a gas syringe too, just like the marble chips and HCl reaction — you measure the volume of gas given off.

Chemistry 2b — Reaction Rates, Salts and Electrolysis

Rate of Reaction Experiments

Q5 When you mix **sodium thiosulfate** solution and **hydrochloric acid**, a precipitate is formed. Underline the correct statement(s) about the reaction.

The precipitate is white.

The mixture goes cloudy.

Sulfur is yellow.

Q6 Yasmin investigates the effect of **temperature** on the rate of the reaction between sodium thiosulfate solution and hydrochloric acid. She mixes the reactants together in a flask and times how long a cross placed under the flask takes to disappear.

a) Circle the items from the following list that she could use to do this.

scales   syringe   water bath   stopclock   thermometer

b) Here are some results from her investigation:

Temperature (°C)	20	30	40	50	60
Time taken for cross to disappear (s)	201	177		112	82

i) As the temperature increases, does the reaction get **faster** or **slower**? ....

ii) One of the values in the table is missing. Circle the most likely value for it from the list below.

145 s   **192 s**   **115 s**

c) i) Name the **independent** variable in this experiment. ....

ii) Name the **dependent** variable in this experiment. ....

d) Suggest one thing Yasmin could do to make her results more **reliable**.

....

....

Q7 Nir uses the sodium thiosulfate and hydrochloric acid reaction to investigate the effect of varying the **concentration** of hydrochloric acid on the rate of reaction. He mixes the reactants together in a flask and times how long it takes for a cross placed under the flask to disappear.

He obtains these results:

Concentration of HCl (mol/dm^3)	2.00	1.75	1.50	1.25	1.00
Time taken for cross to disappear (s)	13	23	38	50	67

What conclusion can Nir draw from these results?

....

Rate of Reaction Experiments

Q8   Hydrogen peroxide **decomposes** into water and oxygen.

a)   Complete the equation for the decomposition of hydrogen peroxide.

$$2H_2O_2 \rightleftharpoons \text{................} + O_2$$

Don't forget it needs to be balanced.

b)   What is a good way to measure the rate of this reaction?
Circle the letter next to the correct answer.

   A   Weigh the amount of water produced

   B   Time how long the reaction takes to go cloudy

   C   Measure the volume of gas produced at regular time intervals

   D   Measure the temperature

c)   Circle the correct word from the pair to complete the sentence.

   We can **increase** / **decrease** the speed of this decomposition reaction by using a catalyst.

Q9   The decomposition of hydrogen peroxide can be used to investigate the effect of a **catalyst** on the rate of reaction. A student compared three different catalysts to see which was the most effective (increased the rate of reaction the most). He used a gas syringe to measure the amount of gas produced. Below is a graph of his results.

a)   Label the y-axis (don't forget to include appropriate units).

b)   The three catalysts used in this experiment were **potato peel**, **blood** and **manganese (IV) oxide**. Manganese (IV) oxide is the most effective catalyst for this reaction.

....

....

R

S

T

Time (s)

   i)   Using the graph, decide which curve (R, S or T) represents the reaction using manganese (IV) oxide. Circle the correct letter.

           R   S   T

   ii) Explain your answer.

   ....

   ....

Collision Theory

Q1 Draw lines to match up the changes with their effects.

increasing the temperature

means fewer particles of reactant are present, so less frequent collisions occur

decreasing the concentration

gives particles a bigger area of solid reactant to react with

increasing the surface area

makes the particles move faster, so they collide more often

Q2 Circle the correct words to complete the following sentences.

a) If you heat up a reaction, you give the particles more **energy** / **surface area**.

b) This makes them move **faster** / **slower** so successful collisions happen **more** / **less** frequently.

c) So, increasing the temperature increases the **concentration** / **rate of reaction**.

Q3 Gases are always under **pressure**.

a) i) If you increase the pressure of a gas reaction, does the rate **increase** or **decrease**?

....

ii) Explain your answer.

....

....

b) In the boxes on the right draw two diagrams — one showing particles of two different gases at low pressure, the other showing the same two gases at high pressure.

low pressure   **high pressure**

Q4 Read the four statements about **surface area** and rate of reaction. Tick the appropriate boxes to show whether they are true or false.

	True	False
a) Breaking a larger solid into smaller pieces decreases its surface area.	☐	☐
b) A larger surface area will mean a faster rate of reaction.	☐	☐
c) A larger surface area decreases how often successful collisions happen.	☐	☐
d) Powdered marble has a larger surface area than an equal mass of marble chips has.	☐	☐

Collision Theory and Catalysts

Q1 What is meant by **activation energy**?

....

....

Q2 **Catalysts** are often used in reactions.

a) What is a catalyst?

....

....

b) The diagram to the right shows two reactions, A and B.
One has a catalyst and one doesn't.

i) Which line shows the reaction
with a catalyst, A or B?

....

ii) Explain your answer.

....

....

Q3 Catalysts are used in many **industrial reactions**.

a) Give **one** reason why catalysts are **useful** for industrial processes.

....

....

b) Give **two** possible **problems** with using catalysts in industrial processes.

1. ....

2. ....

c) Name an industrial process and the catalyst it uses.

....

Top Tips: Unlike other exciting things, such as chocolate buttons and a fashion for sparkly leggings, a catalyst isn't used up or changed — so you can use it again and again... and again.

Energy Transfer in Reactions

Q1 Circle the correct words from each pair in this paragraph about **exothermic** reactions.

> Exothermic reactions transfer energy **to** / **from** the surroundings, usually in the
> form of **heat** / **sound**. This is often shown by a **fall** / **rise** in **temperature** / **mass**.

Q2 Three examples of exothermic reactions are **burning fuels**, **neutralisation** and **oxidation**.

a) Write **B** for burning fuel or **N** for neutralisation reaction next to each of the following reactions.

☐ acid + alkali → salt + water

☐ petrol + oxygen → carbon dioxide + water

b) Give another word for 'burning'. ....

c) Give an example of an oxidation reaction.

....

Q3 Fill in the missing words in this paragraph about **endothermic** reactions.

> Endothermic reactions .... energy from the surroundings,
> usually in the form of ....
> This is often shown by a .... in temperature.

Q4 Limestone ($CaCO_3$) breaks down when heated to form quicklime and carbon dioxide.

a) What type of reaction is this?

....

b) The reaction requires a large amount of heat.

i) Is it **exothermic** or **endothermic**? ....

ii) Explain your answer ....

c) Breaking down 1 tonne (1000 kg) of $CaCO_3$ requires about 1 800 000 kJ of heat energy.

i) How much heat energy would be needed to make **1 kg** of $CaCO_3$ break down?

....

ii) How much $CaCO_3$ could be broken down by **90 000 kJ** of heat energy?

....

Energy Transfer in Reactions

Q5   Sam did an experiment to investigate the **thermal decomposition** of **copper sulfate**. He wrote this about his investigation:

"When I heated up blue copper sulfate it steamed and went white. After it cooled down I dropped a little water on it and it got really hot and turned blue again".

Water vapour

Answer these questions about Sam's observations:

a)   Which part of Sam's experiment was exothermic? ....

b)   Which part of Sam's experiment was endothermic? ....

c)   Is blue copper sulfate **anhydrous** or **hydrated**? Circle the correct answer.

anhydrous

hydrated

Anhydrous means without water and hydrated means containing water.

d)   Write a **word equation** for this reaction in the box below.

....

⇌   + ...

....

e)   What is a reaction that can go both ways called?

....

Q6   Here are some practical uses of chemical reactions. Decide whether each reaction is endothermic or exothermic. In the box, put **N** for endothermic and **X** for exothermic.

a)   A camping stove burns methylated spirit to heat a pan of beans.   ☐

b)   Special chemical cool packs are used by athletes to treat injuries. They take heat in and the pack becomes very cold.   ☐

c)   Self-heating cans of coffee contain chemicals in the base. When the chemicals are combined they produce heat which warms the can.   ☐

d)   Baking powder is used to make cakes rise. When it's heated in the oven it thermally decomposes to produce a gas.   ☐

Top Tips: Anything that takes heat in is endothermic. Endothermic reactions are pretty rare in everyday life but they do occur — think about cooking eggs or even melting ice cream in your mouth.

Acids and Alkalis

Q1 a) Complete the equation below for the reaction between an acid and a base.

acid + base → .... + ...

b) Circle the correct term for this kind of reaction.

decomposition   oxidation   neutralisation

c) Which of the following ions:

$$H^+_{(aq)} \quad OH^-_{(aq)} \quad Cl^-_{(aq)} \quad Na^+_{(aq)}$$

i) react with each other to form water?   ....

ii) is present in an acidic solution?   ....

iii) is present in an alkaline solution?   ....

iv) would be present in a solution with a pH of 10?   ....

v) would be present in a solution with a pH of 2?   ....

Q2 Complete the following sentences.

a) Solutions which are not acidic or alkaline are said to be ....

b) An example of an indicator is ....

c) If a substance is neutral it has a pH of ....

d) A soluble base is known as an ....

Q3 Joey wanted to make **sodium chloride** (a salt) by adding hydrochloric acid to sodium hydroxide solution.

a) Complete the **symbol equation** below for this reaction.

$HCl_{(aq)}$ + $NaOH_{(aq)}$ → .... + ...

b) Write an equation to show the reaction between hydrogen ions and hydroxide ions in this reaction.

....

c) Suggest what Joey could use to tell whether the reaction was **over**.

....

d) What would the pH of the products be?

....

Acids and Alkalis

Q4   State symbols give the **physical state** of a substance.

Give the **symbols** for the following states.

a) Solid ☐   **c)** Gas ☐

b) Liquid ☐   **d)** Dissolved in water (aqueous) ☐

Q5   Ants' stings hurt because of the **formic acid** they release.

Substance	pH
lemon juice	4
baking soda	9
caustic soda	14
soap powder	11

a) The table to the right shows the pH measurements of some household substances. Suggest a substance from the list that could be used to relieve the discomfort of an ant sting.

....

b) Explain your answer.

....

....

....

Q6   Joey wanted to test whether some antacid tablets really do **neutralise acid**.

He added a tablet to some hydrochloric acid, stirred it until it dissolved and tested the pH of the solution. He carried out further tests after dissolving a second, third and fourth tablet. His results are shown in the table below.

Number of Tablets	pH
0	1
1	2
2	3
3	7
4	9

a) Plot a graph of the results.

b) Describe how the pH changes when antacid tablets are added to the acid.

....

c) How many tablets were needed to neutralise the acid? ....

Top Tips: State symbols might look like an afterthought but they provide pretty important information about a reaction. You need to know whether your products are going to be liquids that you can contain in a flask, or gases that'll need a bung to stop them floating off around the room.

Chemistry 2b — Reaction Rates, Salts and Electrolysis

Acids Reacting With Metals

Q1   The diagram below shows **aluminium** reacting with **sulfuric acid**.

a)   Label the diagram with the names of the chemicals.

....

....

....

b)   Complete the word equation for this reaction:

aluminium + ... → **aluminium sulfate +** ....

c)   Write a balanced symbol equation for this reaction.

....

The formula of aluminium sulfate is $Al_2(SO_4)_3$.

d)   Zinc also reacts with sulfuric acid. Give the word equation for this reaction.

....

e)   Write a balanced symbol equation for the reaction between magnesium and hydrochloric acid.

....

Q2   The table shows what happens when different **metals** react with **hydrochloric acid**.

Metal	A	B	C	D
Observations	gas bubbles formed vigorously metal disappeared quickly	no gas bubbles formed metal unaffected by the acid	gas bubbles form slowly most of the metal remained after 5 min	gas bubbles form steadily most of the metal disappeared after 5 min

a)   Which of A-D is the **most** reactive metal? ....

most reactive

b)   Which of metals A-D are **less** reactive than hydrogen? ....

magnesium

c)   The metals used in this experiment were **magnesium**, **zinc**, **iron** and **copper**. Using the reactivity series on the right to help you, match each of these metals to the correct letter from the table.

zinc

iron

A ....   C ....

hydrogen

B ....   D ....

copper

least reactive

Acids Reacting With Metals

Q3 Rhiannon is planning an experiment to investigate the rate of reaction between magnesium and different **concentrations** of hydrochloric acid.

a) How could she measure the rate of the reaction?

....

b) What is the **independent variable** in her experiment?

....

c) Give two variables that she will need to keep the **same** in her experiment.

....

Q4 Fill in the blanks using some of the words given below.

reactive	copper	nitric	more	hydrogen	less	chloride
sulfuric	carbon dioxide	non-metals	nitrate	metals		

Acids react with most .... to form salts and .... gas.

Metals like .... and silver which are less .... than

hydrogen don't react with acids. The .... reactive the metal, the more

vigorously the bubbles of gas form. Hydrochloric acid forms .... salts

and .... acid produces sulfate salts. However, the reactions of metals

with .... acid don't follow this simple pattern.

Q5 a) Write out the **balanced** versions of the following equations.

i) $Ca + HCl \rightarrow CaCl_2 + H_2$ ....

ii) $Na + HCl \rightarrow NaCl + H_2$ ....

iii) $Li + H_2SO_4 \rightarrow Li_2SO_4 + H_2$ ....

b) Hydrobromic acid reacts with magnesium as shown in the equation below to form a bromide salt and hydrogen.

$$Mg + 2HBr \rightarrow MgBr_2 + H_2$$

i) Name the salt formed in this reaction. ....

ii) Write a balanced symbol equation for the reaction between aluminium and hydrobromic acid. (The formula of aluminium bromide is $AlBr_3$.)

....

Oxides, Hydroxides and Ammonia

Q1   Fill in the blanks to complete the word equations for **acids** reacting with **metal oxides** and **metal hydroxides**.

a)   hydrochloric acid + lead oxide → .... chloride + water

b)   nitric acid + copper hydroxide → copper .... + water

c)   sulfuric acid + zinc oxide → zinc sulfate + ...

d)   hydrochloric acid + ... oxide → nickel .... + ...

e)   .... acid + copper oxide → .... nitrate + ...

f)   sulfuric acid + ... hydroxide → sodium .... + ...

Q2 a)   Put a tick in the box next to any of the sentences below which are **true**.

Alkalis are bases which don't dissolve in water.

Acids react with metal oxides to form a salt and water.

Hydrogen gas is formed when an acid reacts with an alkali.

Salts and water are formed when acids react with metal hydroxides.

Ammonia solution is alkaline.

Calcium hydroxide is an acid that dissolves in water.

b)   Use the formulas below to write **symbol equations** for two acid/base reactions.

H_2SO_4 H_2O CuO $NaCl$ HCl $CuSO_4$ H_2O $NaOH$

....

....

Q3   Name two substances which would react to make each of the following **salts**.

a)   Potassium sulfate ....

b)   Ammonium chloride ....

c)   Silver nitrate ....

92

Oxides, Hydroxides and Ammonia

Q4 **Ammonia** can be neutralised by **nitric acid** to form a salt.

a) Underline the correct formula for ammonia below.

NH_4NO_3 NH_4Cl NH_3 NH_2 NH_4

b) Fill in the blanks in the passage below using some of the words from the list.

proteins	solid	fertilisers	acidic	nitrogen	liquid	salts	alkaline

Ammonia dissolves in water to form an .... solution. Ammonia contains

.... which plants need to produce ...., so it is used to

make ammonium .... which are widely used as ....

c) Write down the word equation for making **ammonium nitrate**.

....

d) Why is ammonium nitrate a particularly good fertiliser?

....

e) How is this neutralisation reaction different from most neutralisation reactions?

....

Q5 a) Complete the following equations.

i) $H_2SO_{4(aq)}$ + ... → $CuSO_{4(aq)}$ + $H_2O_{(l)}$

ii) $2HNO_{3(aq)}$ + $MgO_{(s)}$ → $Mg(NO_3)_{2(aq)}$ + ...

iii) .... + $KOH_{(aq)}$ → $KCl_{(aq)}$ + $H_2O_{(l)}$

iv) $2HCl_{(aq)}$ + ... → $ZnCl_{2(aq)}$ + $H_2O_{(l)}$

v) $H_2SO_{4(aq)}$ + $2NaOH_{(aq)}$ → .... + ...

b) **Balance** the following acid/base reactions.

i) $NaOH$ + H_2SO_4 → Na_2SO_4 + H_2O

ii) $Mg(OH)_2$ + HNO_3 → $Mg(NO_3)_2$ + H_2O

iii) NH_3 + H_2SO_4 → $(NH_4)_2SO_4$

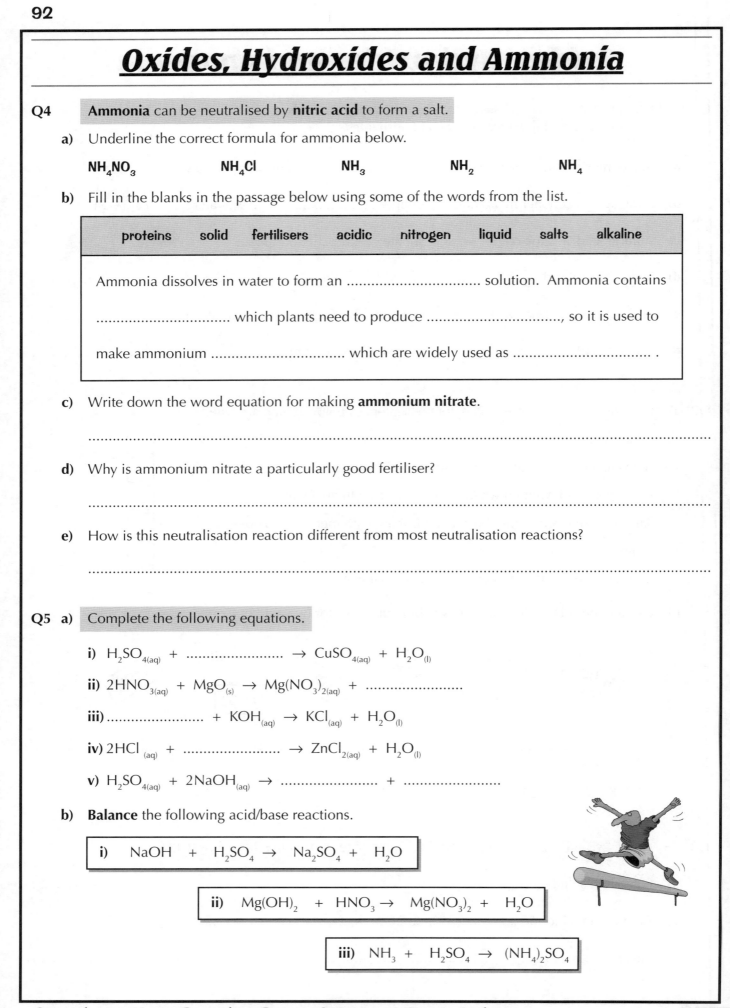

Chemistry 2b — Reaction Rates, Salts and Electrolysis

Making Salts

Q1   Complete the following sentences by circling the correct word from each pair.

a)   Most chlorides, sulfates and nitrates are **soluble** / **insoluble** in water.

b)   Most oxides and hydroxides are **soluble** / **insoluble** in water.

c)   Soluble salts can be made by reacting **acids** / **alkalis** with insoluble bases until they are just **neutralised** / **displaced**.

d)   Insoluble salts are made by **precipitation** / **electrolysis**.

Q2   **A**, **B** and **C** are symbol equations for reactions in which **salts** are formed.

$$A \qquad CuO_{(s)} \ + \ H_2SO_{4(aq)} \ \rightarrow \ CuSO_{4(aq)} \ + \ H_2O_{(l)}$$

$$B \qquad 2NaOH_{(aq)} \ + \ H_2SO_{4(aq)} \ \rightarrow \ Na_2SO_{4(aq)} \ + \ 2H_2O_{(l)}$$

$$C \qquad Pb(NO_3)_{2(aq)} \ + \ H_2SO_{4(aq)} \ \rightarrow \ PbSO_{4(s)} \ + \ 2HNO_{3(aq)}$$

Which equation (A, B, C) refers to the formation of a salt:

a)   in an acid/alkali reaction ....

b)   by precipitation ....

c)   from an insoluble base ....

Q3   **Silver chloride** is an insoluble salt which is formed as a **precipitate** when silver nitrate and sodium chloride solutions are mixed together.

a)   Complete the word equation for the reaction.

.... + ... → silver chloride + ...

b)   After mixing the solutions to produce a precipitate, what further steps are needed to produce a dry sample of silver chloride?

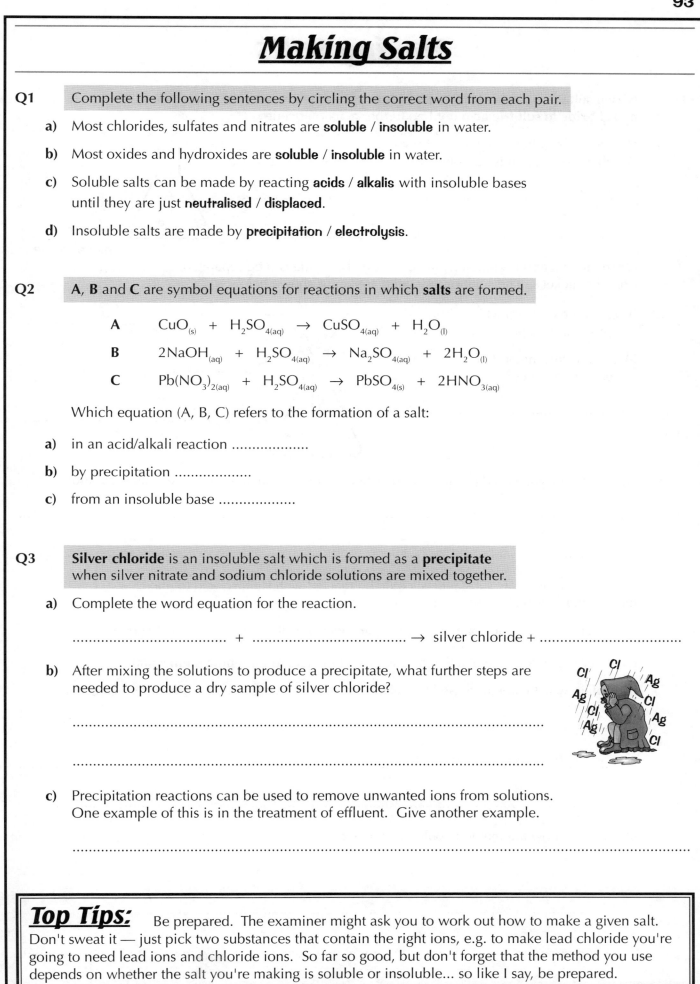

....

....

c)   Precipitation reactions can be used to remove unwanted ions from solutions. One example of this is in the treatment of effluent. Give another example.

....

Top Tips: Be prepared. The examiner might ask you to work out how to make a given salt. Don't sweat it — just pick two substances that contain the right ions, e.g. to make lead chloride you're going to need lead ions and chloride ions. So far so good, but don't forget that the method you use depends on whether the salt you're making is soluble or insoluble... so like I say, be prepared.

Making Salts

Q4   **Nickel sulfate** (a soluble salt) can be made by adding an excess of insoluble **nickel oxide** to **sulfuric acid** until no further reaction occurs.

a) Give an observation that would show you that the reaction is complete.

....

....

acid

excess of nickel oxide

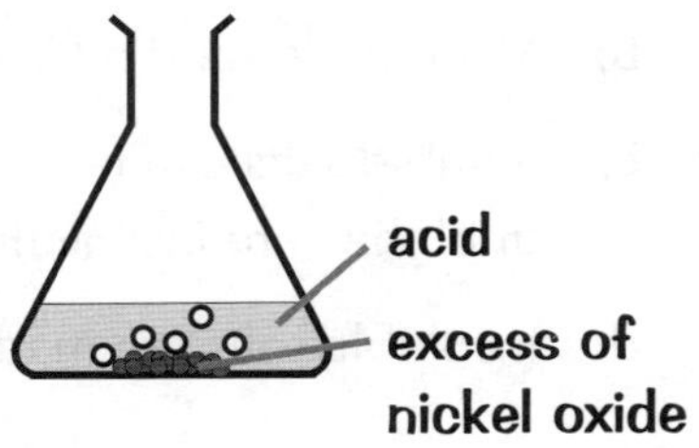

Once the reaction is complete, the excess nickel oxide can be separated from the nickel sulfate solution using the apparatus shown below.

b) i) Label the diagram which shows the separation process.

....

ii) What is this method of separation called?

....

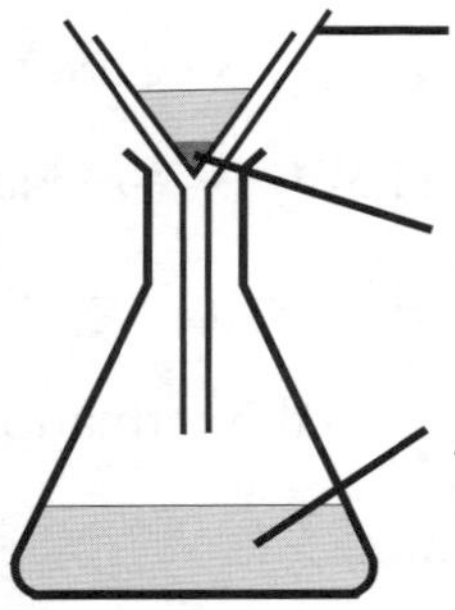

....

....

c) Describe how you could produce solid crystals of nickel sulfate from nickel sulfate solution.

....

....

d) Which other insoluble substance(s) could be reacted with sulfuric acid to make **nickel sulfate** using this method? Circle the correct answer(s) below.

nickel   lead chloride   ammonium sulfate   nickel hydroxide

e) Potassium hydroxide, an **alkali**, reacts with sulfuric acid to form **potassium sulfate**.

i) Explain why the method used to make nickel sulfate needs to be modified for this reaction.

....

....

....

ii) Describe how the method could be changed.

....

....

....

Electrolysis

Q1   Fill in the blanks in the passage below using the words provided.

electric current	liquid	conduct	atoms	electrolysis	molecules
flow	positive	elements	negative	ionic	free ions	molten

If you pass an .... through an ....

substance that's .... or in solution, it breaks down into the

.... it's made of. This is called ....

It requires a .... to conduct the electricity, called the electrolyte.

Electrolytes contain .... which ....

the electricity. For an electrical circuit to be complete, there's got to be a

.... of electrons. Electrons are taken away from ions at the

.... electrode and given to other ions at the

.... electrode. As ions gain or lose electrons they become

.... or .... and are released.

Q2   **Lead bromide** is an ionic substance. It doesn't easily dissolve in water.

a)   How could lead bromide be made into a liquid for electrolysis?

....

b)   Give the **products** of the electrolysis of lead bromide.

....

c)   Tick the correct boxes to show whether the following statements
about the electrolysis of **lead bromide** are **true** or **false**.

True   False

i)   The bromide ions are oxidised.   ☐   ☐

ii) Bromide ions are attracted to the negative electrode.   ☐   ☐

iii) At the negative electrode, positively charged ions gain electrons.   ☐   ☐

iv) Lead atoms become lead ions at the negative electrode.   ☐   ☐

v)   Oxidation is a gain of electrons.   ☐   ☐

Top Tips: You probably tend to think of oxidation and reduction as gain or loss of oxygen.
That's not wrong, but it's not always true either — it can refer to electrons being lost or gained.

Electrolysis of Sodium Chloride Solution

Q1 The table shows the products at the negative electrode when different solutions of **ionic substances** are electrolysed.

a) What do you notice about the product released at the negative electrode and its position in the reactivity series?

....

....

....

Ionic Substance in Solution	Product at Negative Electrode
sodium nitrate	hydrogen
copper sulfate	copper
zinc iodide	hydrogen
potassium chloride	hydrogen
silver nitrate	silver

reactivity →

potassium
sodium
calcium
carbon
zinc
iron
lead
hydrogen
copper
silver

b) A solution of iron chloride is electrolysed. What product would form at the negative electrode?

....

Q2 Use the words below to complete the passage about the electrolysis of **sodium chloride solution**.

chlorine   soap   sodium chloride   sodium hydroxide   plastics   bleach   negative electrode

During the electrolysis, ... is split into three useful products.

At the positive electrode .... gas is produced. This can be used in

the manufacture of .... and ....

At the .... hydrogen gas is given off. ....

is left in solution. This strong alkali is used to make ....

Q3 The diagram below shows the electrolysis of a **salt solution**.

a) Identify the ions and molecules labelled A, B, C and D on the diagram. Choose from the options in the box below.

Na^+ H^+ Cl_2 H_2 Cl^- Na_2 H_2O

A ....

B ....

C ....

D ....

Negative Electrode (-ve)   Positive Electrode (+ve)

C   D

A   B

NaCl Solution

b) Write **balanced** half-equations for the processes that occur at the electrodes during the electrolysis of this salt solution.

Positive electrode: ....

Negative electrode: ....

Make sure the charges balance.

Extraction of Aluminium and Electroplating

Q1 **Aluminium** is the most **abundant** metal in the Earth's crust.

Goodness, how awfully common... °₀₀°

a) **i)** Circle the correct word:

The most common aluminium ore is **bauxite / cryolite.**

ii) When this ore is mined and purified, which compound is obtained? Give its name and formula.

Name .... Formula ....

b) Tick the boxes to show whether the following statements are **true** or **false**.

True False

i) In the extraction of aluminium the electrolyte is molten aluminium metal. ☐ ☐

ii) Aluminium oxide is dissolved in molten cryolite before electrolysis begins. ☐ ☐

iii) Cryolite is used in the electrolysis of aluminium to keep the cost down. ☐ ☐

iv) Copper electrodes are used in the extraction of aluminium by electrolysis. ☐ ☐

v) Aluminium is formed at the positive electrode. ☐ ☐

c) The positive electrode needs to be **replaced** frequently. Explain why.

....

....

Q2 Electroplating could be used to put a thin coat of **silver** onto a **nickel** fork.

a) Complete the diagram below by labelling the **negative electrode** and **positive electrode**.

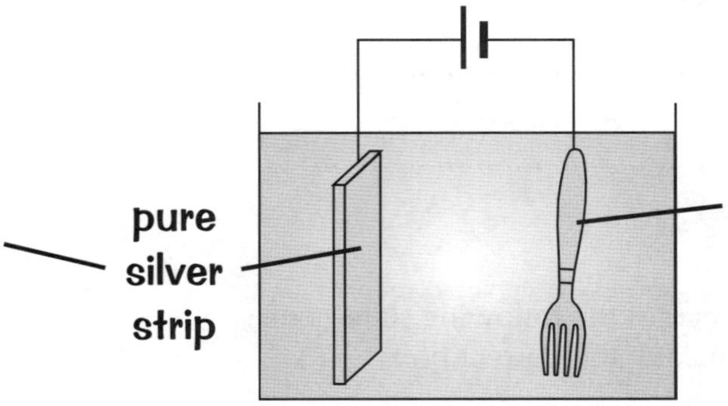

.... pure silver strip ....

b) What **ion** must the electrolyte contain?

....

c) Give **one** reason why you might want to electroplate a nickel fork with silver.

....

d) Give **one** other use of electroplating.

....

<u>*Mixed Questions — Chemistry 2b*</u>

Q1 Several factors affect **how quickly** chemical reactions occur.

a) Name four things that can **increase** the rate of a reaction.

1. .... 2. ....

3. .... 4. ....

b) Measuring the **amount of reactant used up** over time is one way to work out the rate of a reaction. Give the other thing that can be measured over time to give the rate of a reaction.

....

Q2 The graph shows the results from an experiment using magnesium and dilute hydrochloric acid. The **change in mass** of the reactants was measured using a balance.

a) Which reaction was **faster**, P or Q?

....

b) Which reaction used the **most** reactants, P, Q or R?

....

c) The reaction produces a **gas**. Which other experimental method could you have used to measure the rate of reaction?

....

....

Q3 Indicate whether each of the following statements is **true** or **false** by ticking the correct box.

	True	False
a) When measuring the change in mass of a reaction, the quicker the reading on the balance drops, the faster the reaction.	☐	☐
b) Using a gas syringe to measure the volume of gas given off is usually quite accurate.	☐	☐
c) An explosion is an example of a slow reaction.	☐	☐
d) On a rate of reaction graph the line with the steepest slope shows the fastest rate of reaction.	☐	☐
e) If the same amount of reactants are used the same amount of product will be produced, regardless of the rate of reaction.	☐	☐

Mixed Questions — Chemistry 2b

Q4 The diagram shows the **pH scale**.

1	2	3	4	5	6	7	8	9	10	11	12	13

↑ black coffee (at 5)   ↑ milk of magnesia (at 10)

a) The pH values of black coffee and milk of magnesia are marked on the diagram.

 i) Is black coffee neutral, acidic or alkaline? ....

 ii) Is milk of magnesia neutral, acidic or alkaline? ....

b) i) Some milk of magnesia is added to some black coffee. A reaction takes place. Name the type of reaction.

 ....

 ii) Would you expect this reaction to be exothermic or endothermic?

 ....

Q5 Rose added a piece of **magnesium** to some **HCl** and watched what happened.

a) Complete and **balance** the chemical equation for the reaction.

 Mg + ... HCl → .... + ...

b) Explain how the **pH** would change as the magnesium was added.

 ....

c) What is the name of the salt formed from magnesium and **sulfuric acid**?

 ....

Q6 Aluminium is extracted from its ore by **electrolysis**.

a) The aluminium ions are attracted to the **negative** electrode.

 i) Explain what happens to the aluminium ions at the negative electrode.

 ....

 ....

 ii) Complete and balance the half-equation for this reaction. Include state symbols.

 $$Al^{3+}_{(aq)} + ... \rightarrow ....$$

b) The **oxygen** ions are attracted to the **positive** electrode. Complete and balance the half-equation for the reaction at the positive electrode. Include state symbols.

 $$2O^{2-}_{(aq)} \rightarrow .... + ...$$

Mixed Questions — Chemistry 2b

Q7 Explain why **cryolite** is used in the electrolysis of aluminium oxide.

....

....

Q8 Some solid **magnesium oxide** was added to **HCl** solution in a test tube. The reactants and the products are shown below, but the equation is **not** balanced. **D** is a mystery product.

$$MgO_{(s)} + HCl_{(aq)} \rightarrow D_{(aq)} + H_2O_{(l)}$$

a) i) Give the chemical formula of substance **D**. ....

ii) Write out a full balanced equation for the above reaction.

....

b) When solid magnesium oxide was added to a substance, **S**, magnesium sulfate and water were formed. Identify S by name or formula.

....

c) State whether metal oxides are **acids** or **bases**. ....

Q9 The electrolysis of **sodium chloride solution** gives useful products that can be used in industry.

a) i) Name the two products that form at the **electrodes**.

1. ....

2. ....

ii) Name an industrial use for one of these products.

....

b) When electrolysis is complete, **sodium hydroxide** (NaOH) remains in solution. Explain why this happens. Refer to reactivity in your answer.

....

....

....

c) Electrolysis is also used for electroplating. What is electroplating?

....

History of the Periodic Table

Q1   Complete the sentences below.

a)   In the modern periodic table, the elements are ordered by their ....

b)   Before this, the known elements were arranged in order by their ....

Q2   Tick the boxes to show whether the following statements about **Mendeleev's** Table of Elements are **true** or **false**.

		True	False
a)	Mendeleev left gaps in the table that were later filled.	☐	☐
b)	Mendeleev arranged the elements in order of increasing atomic number.	☐	☐
c)	Mendeleev was able to predict the properties of undiscovered elements.	☐	☐
d)	Elements with similar properties appeared in the same rows.	☐	☐

Q3   Mendeleev left **gaps** in his Table of Elements to keep elements with similar properties in the same groups. He predicted that elements would eventually be discovered to fill the gaps. For example, he predicted the discovery of an element that would fill a gap in his Group 4 and called it **'ekasilicon'**.

Element	Density g/cm^3
carbon	2.27
silicon	2.33
'ekasilicon'	
tin	7.29
lead	11.34

The table shows the **densities** of known elements in this group.

a)   'Ekasilicon' was eventually discovered and given another name.
Use the information in the table to decide which of the elements below is 'ekasilicon'.
Circle your choice.

palladium, 12.02 g/cm³   **germanium, 5.32 g/cm³**   **beryllium, 1.85 g/cm³**   **copper, 8.93 g/cm³**

b)   i)   Before Mendeleev, **Newlands** had already tried to classify the known elements.
Give **one** similarity between Mendeleev's arrangement and Newlands' earlier attempt.

....

ii) What was the main **difference** between their approaches?

....

iii) Give **one problem** with Newlands' attempt.

....

Q4   Explain where the modern **periodic table** gets its name from.

....

....

The Modern Periodic Table

Q1 Use the words below to complete the passage about the periodic table.

properties	fun	chemical	atomic number	predicting	discovered

At first scientists just treated the periodic table as a bit of ....

However, scientists started to realise that the periodic table could be a useful tool for

.... the .... of elements. Once electrons,

protons and neutrons were ...., the periodic table was arranged in

order of .... The electronic structure of elements can then be used

to predict their .... properties.

Q2 The **electron arrangements** of some atoms are shown below.

a) In which of these atoms is the outermost electron **furthest** from the nucleus? ....

b) In which of these atoms is the outermost electron **least shielded** from the nucleus? ....

c) In which of these atoms is the outermost electron **most easily lost**? ....

Q3 A periodic table is shown with **electronic structures** for some of the elements.

0

			H 1						He 2
1	2			3	4	5	6	7	
Li 2,1	Be 2,2			B 2,3	C 2,4	N 2,5	O	F 2,7	Ne 2,8
Na 2,8,1	Mg			Al 2,8,3	Si 2,8,4	P 2,8,5	S	Cl 2,8,7	Ar 2,8,8
K 2,8,8,1	Ca 2,8,8,2	Transition metals							

a) How does the number of electrons in the outer shell of each atom relate to the **group** it is in?

....

b) Write down the electronic structures for:

magnesium .... oxygen .... sulfur ....

c) Is fluorine likely to be more or less reactive than chlorine? Explain your answer.

....

....

The Modern Periodic Table

Q4 The table shows the electronic structure for some **Group 1** and **Group 7** elements.

It's an element, my dear Watson

Group 1	Electronic Structure	Group 7	Electronic Structure
Li	2, 1	F	2, 7
Na	2, 8, 1	Cl	2, 8, 7
K	2, 8, 8, 1	Br	2, 8, 18, 7

Bromine's got more than 8 electrons in one of its shells — don't worry about that for now. The important thing is the number of electrons in its outer shell.

a) **i)** Why do potassium atoms lose their outer electron more easily than lithium atoms?

....

....

ii) Does this make potassium more or less reactive than lithium? ....

b) **i)** Explain why fluorine atoms attract electrons more strongly than bromine atoms.

....

....

ii) Explain the trend in the reactivities of the Group 7 elements in terms of nuclear attraction.

....

....

Q5 The electron arrangement for **potassium** is shown to the right.

a) In which group of the periodic table would you expect to find potassium?

....

b) There are two elements in the same group as potassium that have smaller atomic numbers. Explain whether you would expect these elements to be more or less reactive than potassium.

....

....

....

....

Group 1 — The Alkali Metals

Q1   Indicate whether the statements below about the alkali metals are **true** or **false**.

		True	False
a)	They are keen to gain electrons to form 1^+ ions.	☐	☐
b)	They always form covalent compounds.	☐	☐
c)	They have to be stored in oil.	☐	☐
d)	Their atoms all have a single electron in the outer shell.	☐	☐
e)	They form solid white compounds that dissolve in water to form white solutions.	☐	☐

Q2   Circle the correct word(s) from each pair to complete the passage below.

Sodium reacts vigorously with water producing **sodium dioxide** / **sodium hydroxide**

and **hydrogen** / **oxygen** gas. When it reacts, it loses its outer **proton** / **electron**,

forming an ionic compound where the sodium ion has a **positive** / **negative** charge.

Q3   The table shows the **reactivity** of some Group 1 metals.

Explain the pattern of reactivity shown in the table.

....

....

Element
Li
Na
K
Rb
Cs

reactivity increases

Q4   Archibald put a piece of **lithium** into a beaker of water.

a) Explain why the lithium floated on top of the water.

....

b) After the reaction had finished, Archibald tested the water with universal indicator. Would the solution be acidic, alkaline or neutral? Circle the correct word.

                acidic   **alkaline**   **neutral**

c) i) Write a **word equation** for the reaction.

....

ii) Write a **balanced symbol equation** for the reaction. Include the state symbols.

....

"squeaky pop!"

Top Tips: It's all about keeping up with the trends. Make sure you know what happens to the properties and reactions of the alkali metals as you go down the periodic table.

Chemistry 3a — Elements, Water and Organic Chemistry

Group 7 — The Halogens

Q1 Say whether these statements are **true** or **false**.

                                                                                         True False

a) Chlorine gas is made up of molecules which each contain three chlorine atoms. ☐ ☐

b) The further down the group a halogen is, the harder it is for it to gain an electron. ☐ ☐

c) Halide ions have a charge of 1^+. ☐ ☐

d) The melting points of the halogens increase down the group. ☐ ☐

Q2 Draw lines to match the phrases and complete the sentences.

The halogens exist as molecules ...   ... to form ionic compounds.

A more reactive halogen ...   ... decreases as you move down the group.

The halogens react with metals ...   ... which are pairs of atoms.

The reactivity of the halogens ...   ... will displace a less reactive one.

Q3 **Iron** can be reacted with **bromine**.
An **orange solid** forms on the sides of the test tube.

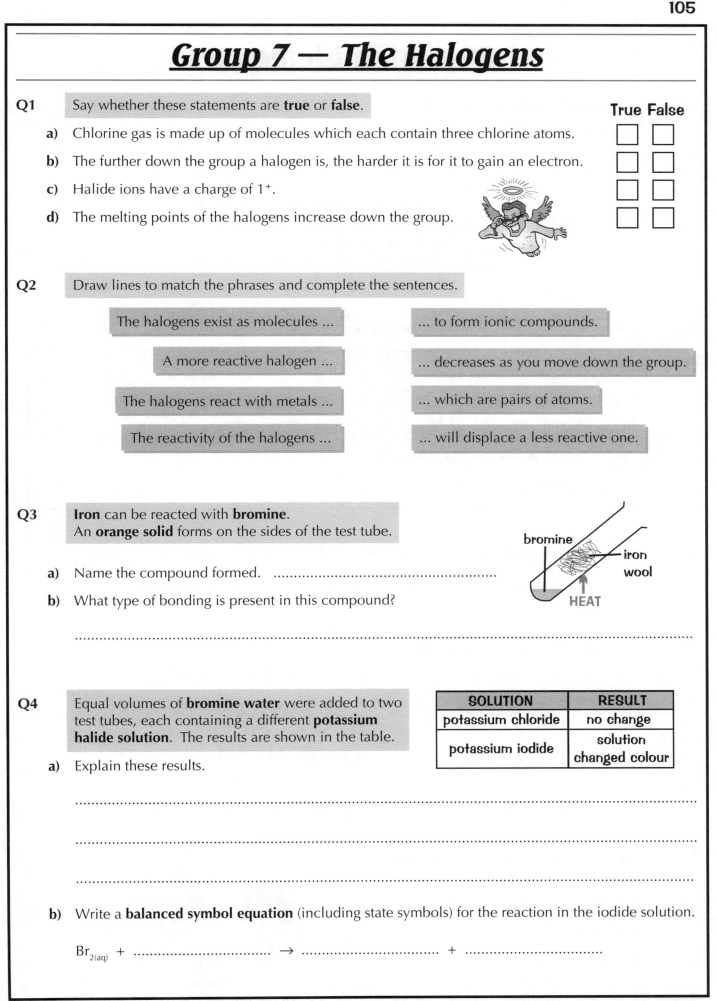

bromine
iron wool
HEAT

a) Name the compound formed. ....

b) What type of bonding is present in this compound?

....

Q4 Equal volumes of **bromine water** were added to two test tubes, each containing a different **potassium halide solution**. The results are shown in the table.

SOLUTION	RESULT
potassium chloride	no change
potassium iodide	solution changed colour

a) Explain these results.

....

....

....

b) Write a **balanced symbol equation** (including state symbols) for the reaction in the iodide solution.

$Br_{2(aq)}$ + ... $\rightarrow$ .... + ...

Chemistry 3a — Elements, Water and Organic Chemistry

Transition Elements

Q1 Transition elements are **metals**.

Shade the area where **transition metals** are found on this periodic table:

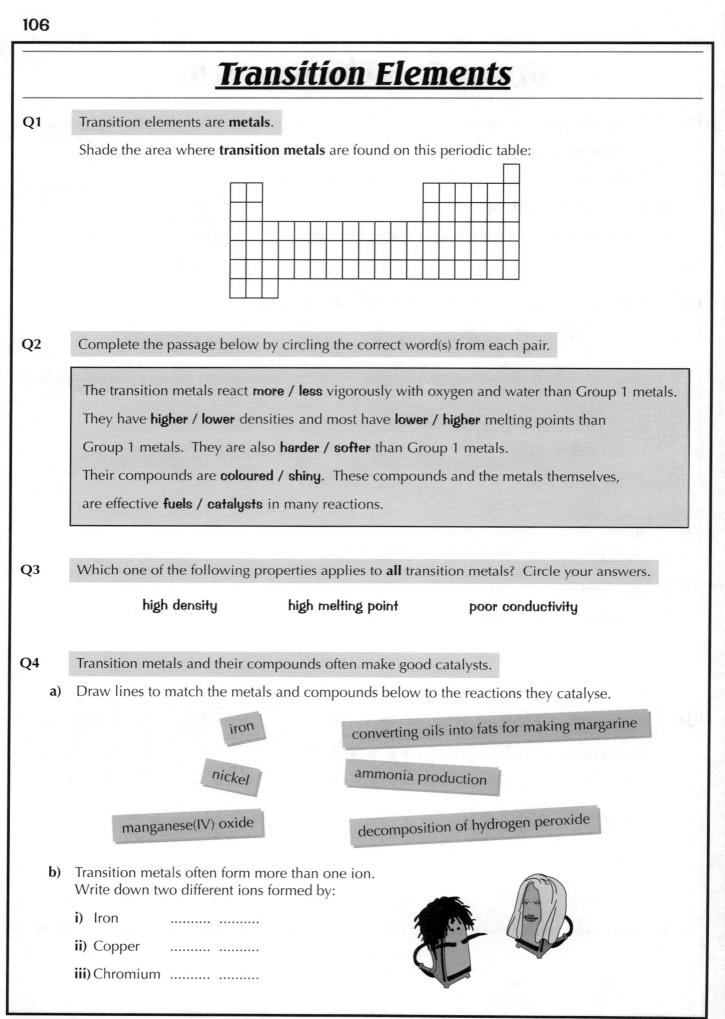

Q2 Complete the passage below by circling the correct word(s) from each pair.

> The transition metals react **more / less** vigorously with oxygen and water than Group 1 metals.
>
> They have **higher / lower** densities and most have **lower / higher** melting points than
>
> Group 1 metals. They are also **harder / softer** than Group 1 metals.
>
> Their compounds are **coloured / shiny**. These compounds and the metals themselves,
>
> are effective **fuels / catalysts** in many reactions.

Q3 Which one of the following properties applies to **all** transition metals? Circle your answers.

high density   **high melting point**   **poor conductivity**

Q4 Transition metals and their compounds often make good catalysts.

a) Draw lines to match the metals and compounds below to the reactions they catalyse.

iron

converting oils into fats for making margarine

nickel

ammonia production

manganese(IV) oxide

decomposition of hydrogen peroxide

b) Transition metals often form more than one ion.
Write down two different ions formed by:

i) Iron   ....

ii) Copper   ....

iii) Chromium   ....

Transition Elements

Q5   'Chemical gardens' can be made by sprinkling **transition metal salts** into **sodium silicate solution**. Transition metal silicate crystals grow upwards as shown.

sodium silicate solution

transition metal silicates

a)   Satoru decides to make a chemical garden. He sprinkles **iron(II) sulfate**, **iron(III) chloride** and **copper sulfate** crystals into sodium silicate solution. What would he see? Circle your answer.

     crystals of different colours   **colourless crystals**

b)   Satoru decides to make another chemical garden. This time he adds **calcium chloride** crystals to the sodium silicate solution. How would the crystals in this chemical garden be **different** from the ones in his first chemical garden? Explain your answer.

....

....

Q6   Read the description of **metal X** and answer the question that follows.

'Metal X is found in the block of elements between groups 2 and 3 in the periodic table. It has a melting point of 1860 °C and a density of 7.2 g/cm³. The metal is used to provide the attractive shiny coating on motorbikes and bathroom taps. The metal forms two coloured chlorides, XCl_2 (blue) and XCl_3 (green).'

Identify six pieces of evidence in the passage which suggest that metal X is a transition metal.

1. ....

2. ....

3. ....

4. ....

5. ....

6. ....

Top Tips: Transition elements do have the properties you would expect a bog standard metal to have. But that's not enough for them so they have some fancy properties of their own. Posers.

Hardness of Water

Q1 State whether the sentences below are true or false.

a) Water which passes over rocks can become hard. ....

b) Water can be softened by removing chloride and carbonate ions from the water. ....

c) Adding sodium chloride is one way of removing hardness from water. ....

d) Scale is formed when soap is used with hard water. ....

e) You can remove the hardness from water by adding sodium carbonate. ....

f) Water hardness is caused by Ca^{2+} and Mg^{2+} ions. ....

g) Soapless detergents do not form scum. ....

h) Less soap is needed to form a lather with hard water. ....

Q2 Hard water can cause the build-up of **scale** in pipes, boilers and kettles.

a) Why can this be a problem with kettles?

....

b) Give two **benefits** of hard water.

1. ....

2. ....

Q3 There are two types of **hardness**.

Draw lines to match the type of hardness to its cause.

| Permanent | Hydrogencarbonate ions |

| Temporary | Dissolved calcium sulfate |

Q4 An **ion exchange column** can be used to remove the hardness from water.

a) Explain how hard water becomes soft when it is passed through an **ion exchange column**.

....

....

b) Does this method work for permanent hardness, temporary hardness, or both?

....

Hardness of Water

Q5 In an experiment to compare the **hardness** of three different water sources, soap solution was added to samples using a burette. Five drops were added at a time until a lasting lather was formed. Fresh samples of the water were boiled and the experiment was repeated.

a) When the samples of hard water were boiled in a beaker, a white precipitate formed.

$$Ca(HCO_3)_{2(aq)} \rightarrow CaCO_{3(s)} + H_2O_{(l)} + CO_{2(g)}$$

Give the chemical name of the white precipitate formed.

....

b) The results for the experiment are shown in the table below.

Source	Drops of soap solution needed to produce a lather using unboiled sample	Drops of soap solution needed to produce a lather using boiled sample
A	35	5
B	30	15
C	5	5

Write the correct letters in the gaps below to complete the sentences about the results.

i) Source .... and .... are hard water.

ii) Source .... contains both temporary and permanent hardness.

iii) Source .... contains only temporary hardness.

iv) Source .... is soft water.

c) i) Explain how you can tell which source contains permanent hardness.

....

ii) Give the name of a chemical that can be added to permanent hard water to soften it.

....

d) i) Suggest which source contains the most temporary hardness. ....

ii) Explain your answer.

....

....

Top Tips: Hard water isn't very exciting, but at least it's not, well, hard. Make sure you know how to soften up the two different types of hardness. Remember that there's more than one tactic.

Water Quality

Q1 **Drinking water** needs to be good quality.

a) Which type of water is most pure? Circle your answer.

   tap water   **river water**   **distilled water**   **sea water**

b) Explain why this type of water is not generally used as drinking water.

....

Q2 Water from reservoirs is treated in a **water treatment works**.

The diagram below shows the stages of a water treatment process.

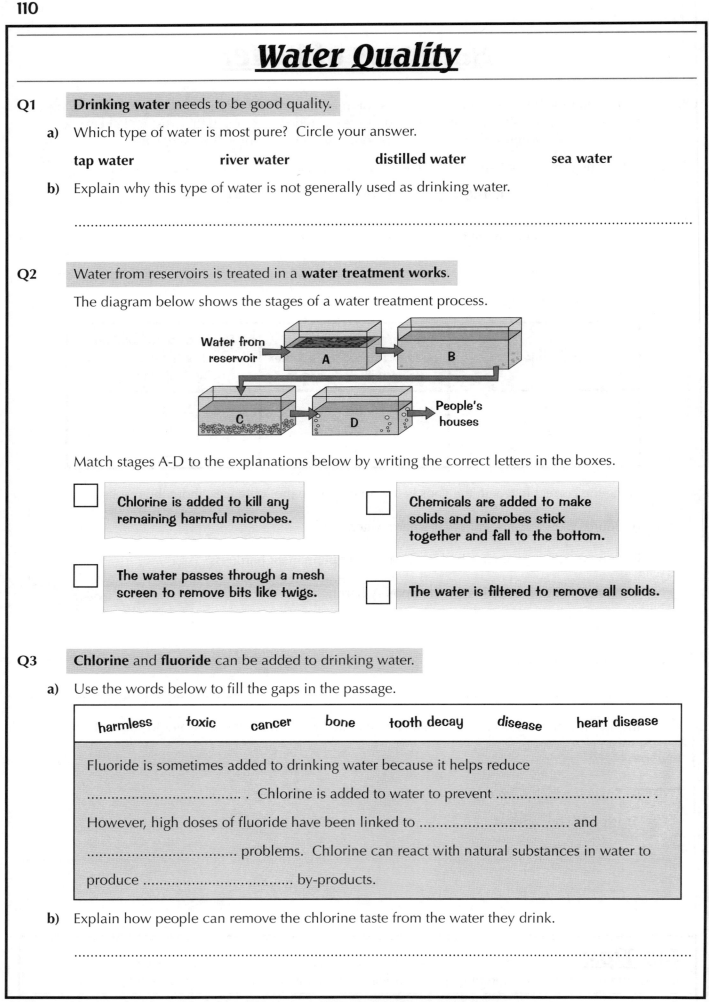

Match stages A-D to the explanations below by writing the correct letters in the boxes.

☐ Chlorine is added to kill any remaining harmful microbes.	☐ Chemicals are added to make solids and microbes stick together and fall to the bottom.
☐ The water passes through a mesh screen to remove bits like twigs.	☐ The water is filtered to remove all solids.

Q3 **Chlorine** and **fluoride** can be added to drinking water.

a) Use the words below to fill the gaps in the passage.

harmless	toxic	cancer	bone	tooth decay	disease	heart disease

Fluoride is sometimes added to drinking water because it helps reduce

.... Chlorine is added to water to prevent ....

However, high doses of fluoride have been linked to .... and

.... problems. Chlorine can react with natural substances in water to

produce .... by-products.

b) Explain how people can remove the chlorine taste from the water they drink.

....

Reversible Reactions

Q1 Use words from the list below to complete the following sentences about **reversible reactions**.

escape	reactants	catalysts	closed	products	react	balance

In a reversible reaction, the .... of the reaction can themselves

.... to give the original ....

At equilibrium, the amounts of reactants and products reach a ....

To reach equilibrium the reaction must happen in a .... system,

where products and reactants can't ....

Q2 Look at this diagram of a **reversible reaction**.

The reaction going from left to right is called the forward reaction.

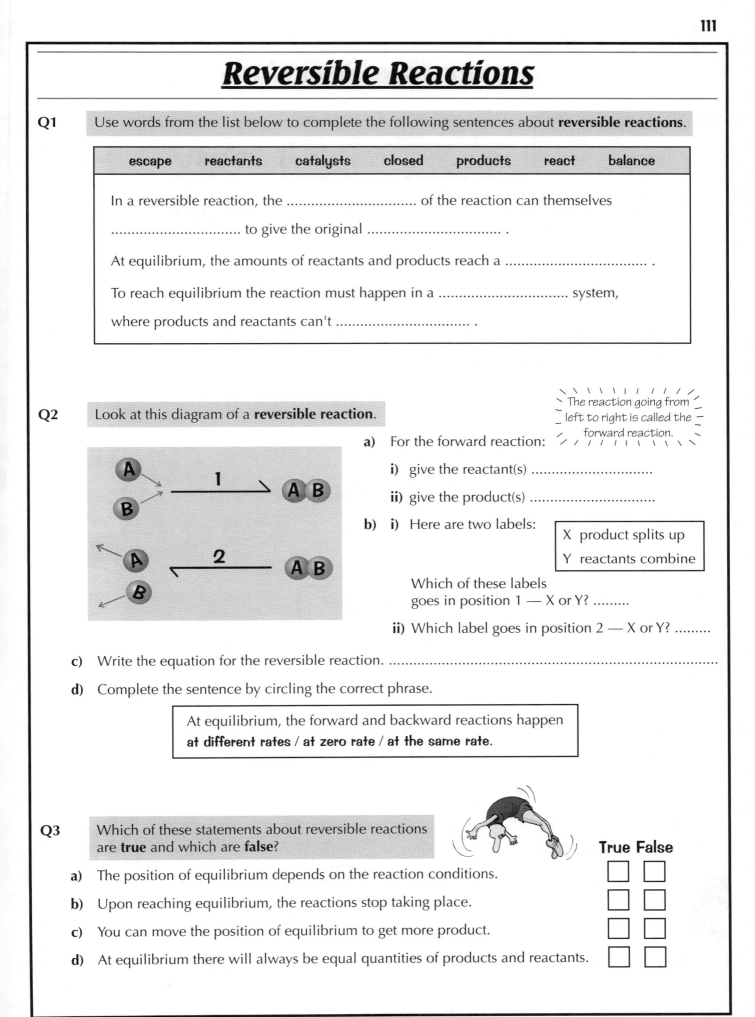

a) For the forward reaction:

   i) give the reactant(s) ....

   ii) give the product(s) ....

b) **i)** Here are two labels:

     | X product splits up |
     | Y reactants combine |

   Which of these labels
   goes in position 1 — X or Y? ....

   ii) Which label goes in position 2 — X or Y? ....

c) Write the equation for the reversible reaction. ....

d) Complete the sentence by circling the correct phrase.

> At equilibrium, the forward and backward reactions happen
> **at different rates / at zero rate / at the same rate.**

Q3 Which of these statements about reversible reactions are **true** and which are **false**?

              True **False**

a) The position of equilibrium depends on the reaction conditions. ☐ ☐

b) Upon reaching equilibrium, the reactions stop taking place. ☐ ☐

c) You can move the position of equilibrium to get more product. ☐ ☐

d) At equilibrium there will always be equal quantities of products and reactants. ☐ ☐

Reversible Reactions

Q4   Substances A and B react to produce substances C and D in a reversible reaction.

$$2A_{(g)} + B_{(g)} \rightleftharpoons 2C_{(g)} + D_{(g)}$$

a)   The forward reaction is **exothermic**.
Does the backward reaction give out or take in heat?
Explain your answer.

....

b)   If the **temperature** is raised, which reaction will increase, the forward or the backward reaction?

....

c)   Explain why changing the temperature of a reversible reaction always affect the
position of equilibrium.

....

....

d)   What effect will changing the **pressure** have on the
position of equilibrium of this reaction? Explain your answer.

Look at the number of molecules on each side of the reaction.

....

Q5 a)   In this reaction: $2SO_{2(g)} + O_{2(g)} \rightleftharpoons 2SO_{3(g)}$

i)   Which reaction, forward or backward, is accompanied by a **decrease** in volume?
Explain your answer.

....

....

ii)   How will increasing the pressure affect the position of equilibrium in this reaction?

....

b)   What does adding a catalyst to a reversible reaction do? Circle the correct letter.

A It moves the equilibrium position towards the products.

B It makes the reaction achieve equilibrium more quickly.

C It moves the equilibrium position towards the reactants.

D It causes a decrease in pressure.

c)   What happens to the amount of product when you use a catalyst? ....

The Haber Process

Q1   The Haber process is used to make **ammonia** which is used to produce fertilisers.

a)   Complete the equation for the reaction below.

$$\text{.....................} + \text{.....................} \rightleftharpoons 2NH_{3(g)}$$

b)   Give one source of each of the two reactants in the forward reaction.

....

Q2   The **industrial conditions** for the Haber process are carefully chosen.

a)   What conditions are used? Tick one box.

☐ 1000 atmospheres, 450 °C   ☐ 200 atmospheres, 1000 °C   ☐ 450 atmospheres, 200 °C   ☐ 200 atmospheres, 450 °C

b)   Give two reasons why the pressure used is chosen.

1. ....

2. ....

Q3   In the Haber process reaction, the forward reaction is **exothermic**.

a)   What effect will raising the temperature have on the **amount** of ammonia formed?

....

b)   Explain why a high temperature is used industrially.

....

c)   What happens to the leftover nitrogen and hydrogen? ....

Q4   The Haber process uses an **iron catalyst**.

a)   What effect does this have on the % yield? ....

b)   Iron catalysts are relatively cheap. What effect does using one have on the **cost** of producing the ammonia? Explain your answer.

....

....

Top Tips: Changing the conditions in a reversible reaction to get more product sounds great, but don't forget that these conditions might be too difficult or expensive for factories to produce, or they might mean a reaction that's too slow to be profitable.

Alcohols

Q1 Alcohols are a common group of chemicals.

Complete the following table.

Alcohol	No. of Carbon Atoms	Molecular Formula	Displayed Formula
Methanol			
	2		
Propanol		C_3H_7OH	

Q2 The molecular formula for **propanol** can be written as C_3H_7OH or as C_3H_8O.

a) What is the functional group found in all alcohols? ....

b) Explain why it is better to write ethanol's formula as C_3H_7OH.

....

Q3 Alcohols are **flammable**.

a) Give the balanced equation for the reaction that takes place when **ethanol** burns completely in air.

....

b) Choose from the words below to complete the paragraph about ethanol.

fuel	diesel	non-renewable	fermentation	lubricant	land
more	renewable	oxidation	sunshine	petrol	less

Ethanol can be mixed with .... and used as a

.... for cars. The more ethanol used in the mixture, the

.... pollution produced. In some countries ethanol is made

by the .... of plants such as sugar cane.

Making ethanol this way uses a natural and .... resource.

The sugar cane can be grown continuously, but you need plenty of

.... and ....

Chemistry 3a — Elements, Water and Organic Chemistry

Alcohols

Q4 Tick the correct boxes to show whether the following statements are **true** or **false**.

		True	False
a)	Ethanol is the third alcohol in the homologous series.	☐	☐
b)	Ethanol is more toxic than methanol.	☐	☐
c)	Ethanol is the main alcohol used in alcoholic drinks.	☐	☐
d)	Alcohols burn to produce sulphur dioxide and water.	☐	☐
e)	The first three alcohols all dissolve completely in water to form neutral solutions.	☐	☐
f)	Ethanol can damage the liver and brain.	☐	☐
g)	Ethanol reacts with sodium to produce sodium ethoxide and hydrogen.	☐	☐

Q5 **Alcohols** can be used as **solvents**.

Complete the following passage by filling in the gaps using the words provided.

water	oils	dissolve	perfumes	fats	solvents

Alcohols such as methanol and ethanol can .... some compounds

that water can, but also substances that water can't — e.g. .... and

.... This makes alcohols very useful ....

in industry. For example, ethanol is used to make .... It can mix

with both the .... (which give the smell) and the

.... (that makes up the bulk).

You can use a word more than once if you need to.

Q6 **Meths** (methylated spirits) is ethanol with other substances added to it.

a) One of these substances is a purply-blue dye. Suggest why this is added.

....

b) Give **two** uses of meths.

1. ....

2. ....

Top Tips: Right, listen up. You need to know the **structures**, **formulas**, **properties** and the **reactions** of alcohols. You also need to be able to evaluate all the useful things you can do with them — like using them as a fuel in cars (but I really wouldn't suggest tipping your dad's favourite whisky into his car — he probably won't be best pleased...).

Carboxylic Acids

Q1 Tick the correct boxes to show whether the following statements are **true** or **false**.

	True	False
a) Carboxylic acids have the functional group –COOH.	☐	☐
b) There are six carbon atoms in every molecule of propanoic acid.	☐	☐
c) Ethanoic acid reacts with sodium carbonate to produce sodium ethanoate and water.	☐	☐

Q2 Complete the following table.

Carboxylic acid	No. of Carbon Atoms	Molecular Formula	Displayed Formula
Methanoic Acid			
	2		
		C_2H_5COOH	

Q3 Ethanoic acid can be made by oxidising ethanol.

a) **i)** What can be used to oxidise ethanol? Circle your answer.

a catalyst   microbes   an ester   vinegar

ii) What else can be used to oxidise ethanol?

....

b) When ethanoic acid is dissolved in water it forms a weak acidic solution.

i) Explain why this is.

....

....

ii) Give the common name for a solution of ethanoic acid.

....

c) Hydrochloric acid is a strong acid. Would you expect a solution of hydrochloric acid to have a higher or lower pH than a solution of ethanoic acid with the same concentration?

....

Esters

Q1   Complete the sentences below by circling the correct word from each pair.

a)   The fruit flavours used in some sweets are made by mixing man-made **esters** / **alcohols** together.

b)   Esters **do** / **don't** mix very well with water, and **do** / **don't** mix well with alcohols.

c)   Some esters **are** / **aren't** volatile.

d)   Many esters are highly **unreactive** / **flammable**, which can lead to a flash **fire** / **flood**.

e)   Esters have the functional group **-COO-** / **-COOH**.

Q2   Look at the **structural formulas** and **chemical names** below.

Circle the ones which refer to **esters**.

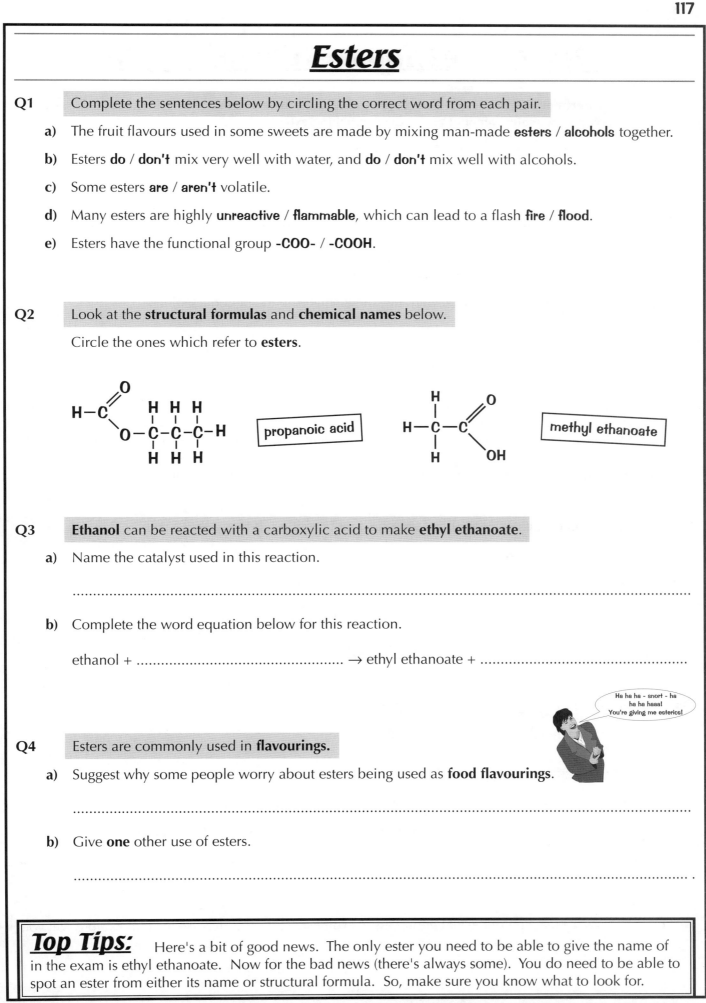

propanoic acid

methyl ethanoate

Q3   **Ethanol** can be reacted with a carboxylic acid to make **ethyl ethanoate**.

a)   Name the catalyst used in this reaction.

....

b)   Complete the word equation below for this reaction.

ethanol + ... → ethyl ethanoate + ...

Ha ha ha - snort - ha
ha ha haaa!
You're giving me esterics!

Q4   Esters are commonly used in **flavourings.**

a)   Suggest why some people worry about esters being used as **food flavourings**.

....

b)   Give **one** other use of esters.

....

Top Tips: Here's a bit of good news. The only ester you need to be able to give the name of in the exam is ethyl ethanoate. Now for the bad news (there's always some). You do need to be able to spot an ester from either its name or structural formula. So, make sure you know what to look for.

Mixed Questions — Chemistry 3a

Q1   A new **perfume**, 'Back2Basics', is being released. The main ingredients are **water**, **alcohol** and a sweet smelling **ester**.

Give **two** properties of esters that make them well suited for use in perfumes.

1. ....

2. ....

Q2   Answer the following questions about the **periodic table**.

a)   By what property did Mendeleev arrange the elements in the periodic table?

....

b)   What did he do that Newlands didn't?

....

c)   If an element is in Group 1, how many electrons will it have in its outer electron shell?   ....

d)   An ion of an element has a 2⁺ charge. Which group is the element most likely to be in?   ....

Q3   **Aqueous chlorine**, Cl_2, was added to **potassium bromide solution**, KBr.

a)   Complete and **balance** the following chemical equation:

$Cl_{2(aq)}$ + ... $KBr_{(aq)}$ → ....(.......) + ...(.......)

b)   Suggest why bromine solution will **not** react with aqueous potassium chloride.

....

Q4   The Haber process is a **reversible reaction**.

a)   Write a **balanced symbol equation** for the reaction.

....

b)   The Haber process is carried out at a pressure of 200 atmospheres.

i) Does raising the pressure **increase** or **decrease** the rate of the forward reaction?   ....

ii) Explain why. ....

....

c)   The forward reaction of the Haber process is **exothermic**. If you **increase** the temperature will you increase or decrease the amount of ammonia produced? Circle the correct answer:

                increase   decrease

Mixed Questions — Chemistry 3a

Q5 The table below contains data for three elements, D, E and F, one of which is a **transition metal**.

Element	Melting point (°C)	Electrical conductivity	Density (g/cm^3)
D	98	good	0.97
E	115	poor	2.07
F	1540	good	7.9

a) Which of the elements is likely to be a transition metal? Give two reasons to justify your answer.

....

....

b) Iron is a typical transition metal. Why is it used in the Haber process?

....

Q6 The elements of Group 1, the alkali metals, are reactive metals.

a) Choose an **element** from the list to answer each of these questions. ⟶
Use the periodic table to help you. Give:

A Rubidium
B Sodium
C Potassium
D Lithium
E Francium
F Caesium

i) an element that is less dense than water. ....

ii) the element with the lowest melting point. ....

iii) the least reactive element. ....

b) Complete the following sentence by circling the correct words.

> Alkali metals always form **covalent** / **ionic** compounds. They react with
> **water** / **air** to produce **hydrogen** / **oxygen** gas and a **hydroxide** / **chloride** solution.

Q7 Hyde added soap solution to samples of water from three different rivers.
He recorded the amount of soap needed to create a lasting lather.

Hyde's results are shown in the table on the right.

RIVER	AMOUNT OF SOAP NEEDED (cm^3)	
	PLAIN WATER	BOILED WATER
A	7	5
B	2	2
C	4	4

a) Which river contained the softest water? ....

b) Which river contained the hardest water? ....

c) Why was less soap needed to form a lasting lather after the water from river A was boiled?

....

....

Titration

Q1 Sulfuric acid reacts with sodium hydroxide to form a **neutral** solution.

Xavier wants to find out how much sulfuric acid is needed to **neutralise** a sample of sodium hydroxide. He decides to carry out a **titration**.

a) During the titration, Xavier will need to use an **indicator**. He is planning to use **universal indicator**.

  i) Explain why this isn't a suitable indicator to use.

  ....

  ....

  ii) Suggest one indicator that Xavier could use instead. ....

b) Write out a step-by-step **method** for Xavier to follow for the titration.

  ....

  ....

  ....

  ....

  ....

  ....

  ....

  ....

c) Draw and label the **apparatus** he should use in the box below.

Titration Calculations

Q1 Work out the number of **moles** in the following solutions.

Remember, no. of moles = conc. × vol.

a) 1 dm³ of 2 mol/dm³ HCl.

....

b) 100 cm³ of 1 mol/dm³ NaOH.

....

c) 25 cm³ of 0.1 mol/dm³ HNO₃.

....

d) 10 cm³ of 0.2 mol/dm³ KOH.

....

Q2 Complete and balance the **symbol equations** for the following acid/alkali reactions.

a) **HCl + NaOH** → .... + ...

Hint: acid + alkali → salt + water.

b) **H₂SO₄ + ... KOH** → .... + ...

Q3 Work out the **masses** and **concentrations** below.

a) Work out the **mass** of acid or alkali present in each solution below.

You can look up relative atomic masses in a periodic table — you don't have to learn them.

i) 0.5 moles of NaOH.

....

ii) 0.2 moles of H₂SO₄.

....

iii) 0.02 moles of Ca(OH)₂.

....

b) Work out the concentration in **g/dm³** of the solutions below.

i) 0.1 mol/dm³ potassium hydroxide (KOH) solution.

....

ii) 2 mol/dm³ nitric acid (HNO₃).

....

Titration Calculations

Q4 The concentration of some sodium hydroxide, **NaOH**, was determined by titration with hydrochloric acid, **HCl**. **25 cm³** of NaOH required **20 cm³** of **0.1 mol/dm³** HCl to neutralise it. Work out the concentration of the NaOH in **g/dm³** using the steps outlined below.

a) How many moles of HCl are present in 20 cm³ of 0.1 mol/dm³ solution?

....

b) Complete the equation for this reaction.

.... + ... → NaCl + ...

c) From the equation, ... mole(s) of HCl reacts with .... mole(s) of NaOH.

d) Use your answer to **c)** to work out how many moles of NaOH there are in 25 cm³ of NaOH.

....

e) What is the concentration of the sodium hydroxide in moles per dm³?

....

f) What is the concentration of the sodium hydroxide in grams per dm³?

....

Q5 In a titration, **10 cm³** of **sulfuric acid solution** was used to neutralise **30 cm³** of **0.1 mol/dm³ potassium hydroxide solution**.

$$H_2SO_4 + 2KOH \rightarrow K_2SO_4 + 2H_2O$$

That's it! I've got the solution!

Big deal. I've got one, too.

a) i) Calculate the number of moles of KOH.

....

ii) Use the equation above to work out how many moles of H_2SO_4 react with the KOH.

....

iii) Calculate the concentration of H_2SO_4 in moles per dm³.

....

b) What is the concentration of the sulfuric acid in grams per dm³?

....

Top Tips: Aargh, calculations. As if Chemistry wasn't tricky enough without maths getting involved too (but at least it's not as bad as Physics). Actually, these aren't the worst calculations as long as you tackle them in stages and know your equations.

Energy

Q1 Use the words to **complete** the blanks in the passage. You can use some words more than once.

| endothermic | exothermic | energy | heat | an increase | a decrease |

All chemical reactions involve changes in .... In ....

reactions, ... energy is given out to the surroundings. A thermometer will show

.... in temperature.

In .... reactions, ... energy is taken in from the

surroundings. A thermometer will show .... in temperature.

Q2 Fiz investigated the **temperature change** during a reaction. She added 25 cm³ of sodium hydroxide solution to 25 cm³ of hydrochloric acid. She used a **data logger** to measure the temperature of the reaction over the first **five** seconds.

The data logger records the temperatures automatically.

Fiz plotted her results on the graph shown to the right.

a) What was the increase in temperature due to the reaction?

....

b) Circle any of the words below that correctly describe the reaction in this experiment.

   neutralisation   combustion

endothermic   respiration   exothermic

c) Why is it difficult to get **an accurate result** for the temperature change in an experiment like this?

....

Q3 **Circle** the correct words to complete each of the sentences below.

a) Energy must be supplied to **break** / **form** bonds.

b) Energy is released when bonds are **broken** / **formed**.

c) Bond breaking is an **exothermic** / **endothermic** process.

d) Bond forming is an **exothermic** / **endothermic** process.

Q4 During the following reaction the reaction mixture's temperature **increases**.

A B + C ➔ A C + B

a) Is the reaction exothermic or endothermic? ....

b) Which bond is stronger, A–B or A–C? Explain your answer. ....

....

Energy and Fuels

Q1   Answer the following questions on **fuels** and **calorimetry**.

a) Why is **copper** often used as the material for calorimetry cans?

....

b) Why is the experimental energy content of a fuel often much less than the actual energy content?

....

Q2   In a calorimetry experiment, **0.7 g** of petrol raised the temperature of **50 g** of water by **30.5 °C**.

a) Given that it takes **4.2 J** to raise the temperature of **1 g** of water by **1 °C**, calculate the energy transferred to the water.

Use:
$Q = mc\Delta T$

....

b) Use your answer to **a)** to calculate the energy produced per gram of petrol. Give your answer in units of **kJ/g**.

....

Q3   A petrol alternative, **fuel X**, has been sent for testing. A scientist tests it using calorimetry. Burning **0.8 g** of fuel X raises the temperature of **50 g** of water by **27 °C**.

a) Calculate the energy produced per gram of fuel X.

....

....

b) Look at your answers to **a)** and **Q2 b)**. Using this evidence only, decide whether petrol or fuel X would make the better fuel. Explain your choice.

....

Q4   There are **environmental** and **economic** consequences of burning fuels.

a) Name the main greenhouse gas released when fossil fuels are burnt. ....

b) Give a possible consequence of increasing levels of greenhouse gases in the atmosphere.

....

c) Explain one potential **economic problem** caused by our reliance on crude oil for fuels.

....

....

....

Bond Energies

Q1 The **energy level diagrams** below represent the energy changes in five chemical reactions.

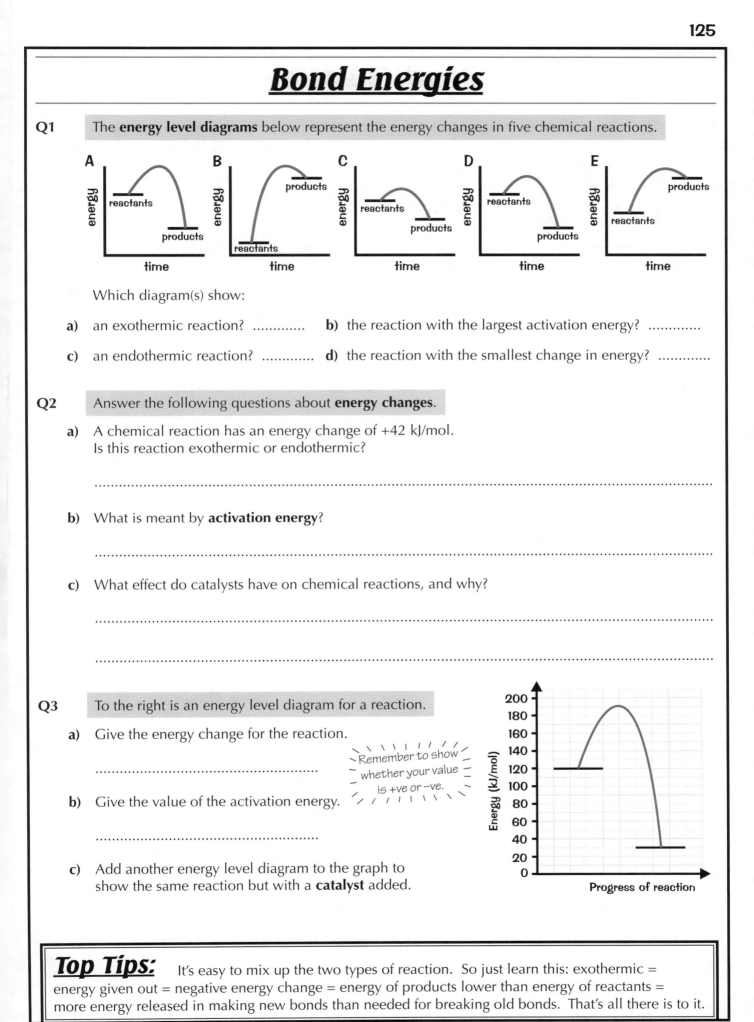

Which diagram(s) show:

a) an exothermic reaction? ....   b) the reaction with the largest activation energy? ....

c) an endothermic reaction? ....   d) the reaction with the smallest change in energy? ....

Q2 Answer the following questions about **energy changes**.

a) A chemical reaction has an energy change of +42 kJ/mol.
Is this reaction exothermic or endothermic?

....

b) What is meant by **activation energy**?

....

c) What effect do catalysts have on chemical reactions, and why?

....

....

Q3 To the right is an energy level diagram for a reaction.

a) Give the energy change for the reaction.

....

b) Give the value of the activation energy.

Remember to show whether your value is +ve or –ve.

....

c) Add another energy level diagram to the graph to
show the same reaction but with a **catalyst** added.

Top Tips: It's easy to mix up the two types of reaction. So just learn this: exothermic =
energy given out = negative energy change = energy of products lower than energy of reactants =
more energy released in making new bonds than needed for breaking old bonds. That's all there is to it.

Chemistry 3b — Titrations, Energy and Chemical Tests

<u>Bond Energies</u>

Q4   The equations below show the combustion of **methane**.

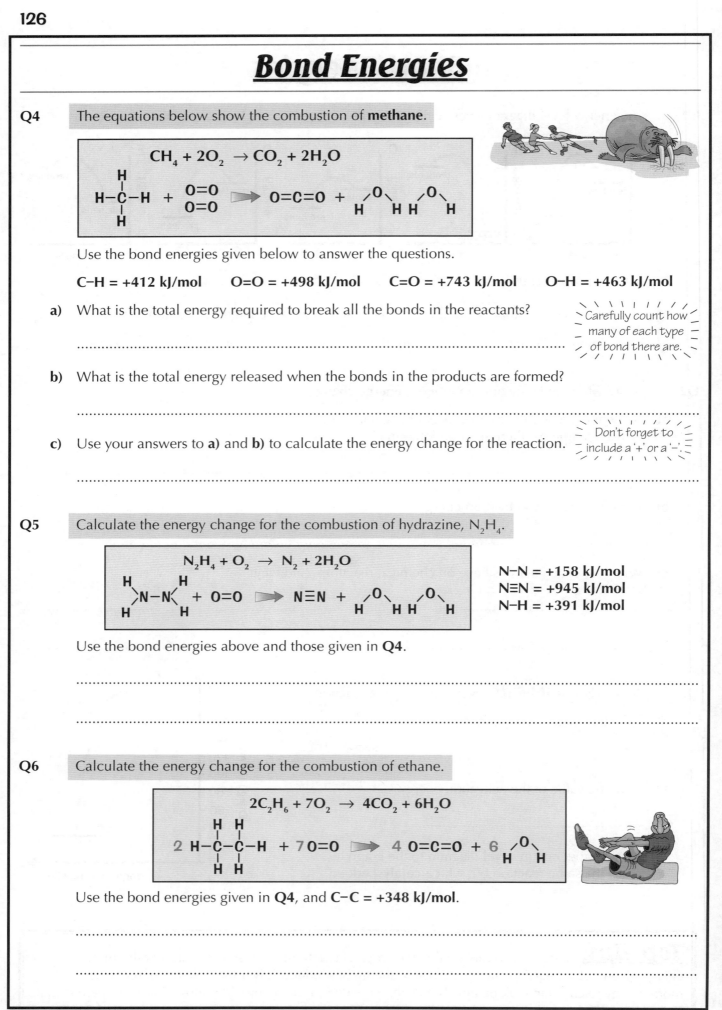

$$CH_4 + 2O_2 \rightarrow CO_2 + 2H_2O$$

Use the bond energies given below to answer the questions.

C–H = +412 kJ/mol   O=O = +498 kJ/mol   C=O = +743 kJ/mol   O–H = +463 kJ/mol

a)   What is the total energy required to break all the bonds in the reactants?

Carefully count how many of each type of bond there are.

....

b)   What is the total energy released when the bonds in the products are formed?

....

c)   Use your answers to **a)** and **b)** to calculate the energy change for the reaction.

Don't forget to include a '+' or a '–'.

....

Q5   Calculate the energy change for the combustion of hydrazine, N_2H_4.

$$N_2H_4 + O_2 \rightarrow N_2 + 2H_2O$$

N–N = +158 kJ/mol
N≡N = +945 kJ/mol
N–H = +391 kJ/mol

Use the bond energies above and those given in **Q4**.

....

....

Q6   Calculate the energy change for the combustion of ethane.

$$2C_2H_6 + 7O_2 \rightarrow 4CO_2 + 6H_2O$$

Use the bond energies given in **Q4**, and **C–C = +348 kJ/mol**.

....

....

Getting Energy from Hydrogen

Q1 Hydrogen and oxygen react together in an **exothermic** reaction.

a) What is the only product when hydrogen and oxygen react together? ....

b) Hydrogen can be burned in oxygen in an internal combustion engine to power a car.

    i) Give **one advantage** of using hydrogen in this way.

    ....

    ii) Give **one disadvantage** of using hydrogen in this way.

    ....

Q2 Fill in the blanks to complete the passage below.

A fuel cell is an electrical cell that's supplied with a ....
and .... and uses energy from the reaction between
them to generate ....

Q3 Cars are being developed that run on fuel cells.

Explain how using these cars could help reduce the amount of air pollution in cities.

....

....

....

Q4 Explain why hydrogen fuel cells are unlikely to mean the end of our dependence on fossil fuels.

....

....

....

....

Tests for Positive Ions

Q1 **Flame tests** are often carried out to identify unknown substances.

a) Complete the statement about **positive ions** below by circling the correct word.

Metals always / don't always form positive ions.

b) Describe how you would use a wire loop to carry out a flame test on an unknown powder.

....

....

....

c) Suggest why the results of this test would be unreliable
if the wire loop used had not been cleaned properly.

....

Q2 Les had five samples of **metal compounds**. He tested each one using a flame test.

a) Draw lines to match each of Les's observations to the
positive metal ion producing the coloured flame.

red flame	Na⁺
yellow flame	Ba²⁺
crimson flame	K⁺
green flame	Ca²⁺
lilac flame	Li⁺

b) Les wants to recommend a compound to use in a firework at a fundraising event for
his local football team. Which of the following compounds should he recommend
in order for the firework to explode in his team's colour, lilac? Circle your answer.

silver nitrate   sodium chloride   barium sulfate

potassium nitrate   calcium carbonate

Top Tips: Right, this stuff needs to be learnt, and learnt properly. Otherwise you'll be stuck in your exam staring at a question about coloured flames and there won't be any sparks upstairs. That's a grim thought. So, snap out of it, think positive, and get learning the science behind the pretty fireworks.

Chemistry 3b — Titrations, Energy and Chemical Tests

Tests for Positive Ions

Q3 Cilla adds a few drops of **NaOH** solution to solutions of different **metal compounds**.

a) Complete her table of results.

Positive Ion	Colour of Precipitate
Fe^{2+}	
	blue
Fe^{3+}	
Al^{3+}	

b) Complete the balanced ionic equation for the reaction of iron(II) ions with hydroxide ions.

$Fe^{2+}_{(\ldots\ldots\ldots)}$ **+** .... $OH^-_{(aq)}$ $\rightarrow$ ....$_{(s)}$

c) Write a balanced ionic equation for the reaction of **iron(III) ions** with hydroxide ions. Include state symbols.

....

d) Cilla adds a few drops of sodium hydroxide solution to **aluminium sulfate solution**. She continues adding sodium hydroxide to excess. What would she observe at each stage?

....

....

Q4 Select compounds from the box to match the following statements.

KCl	LiCl	$FeSO_4$	$FeCl_3$	$Al_2(SO_4)_3$
NaCl	$CuSO_4$	$CaCl_2$	$MgCl_2$	$BaCl_2$

$FeSO_4$ contains Fe^{2+} ions. $FeCl_3$ contains Fe^{3+} ions.

a) This compound forms a blue precipitate with sodium hydroxide solution. ....

b) This compound gives a crimson flame in a flame test. ....

c) This compound forms a white precipitate with sodium hydroxide **that dissolves if excess sodium hydroxide is added.** ....

d) This compound forms a green precipitate with sodium hydroxide solution. ....

e) This compound forms a brown precipitate with sodium hydroxide solution. ....

f) This compound reacts with sodium hydroxide to form a white precipitate, **and it also gives a red flame in a flame test.** ....

Tests for Negative Ions

Q1 Give the chemical formula and charge of the **negative ions** present in the following compounds.

a) barium sulfate ....

b) potassium iodide ....

c) magnesium carbonate ....

Q2 Use the words given to complete the passage below.

carbon dioxide	alkali	limewater	acid	hydrogen

A test for the presence of carbonates in an unidentified substance involves reacting it

with dilute .... If carbonates are present then

.... will be formed. You can test for this by bubbling it through

.... to see if it becomes milky.

Q3 Answer the following questions on testing for **sulfate ions**.

a) Which two reactants are used to test for sulfate ions?

....

b) What would you see after adding these reactants to a sulfate compound?

....

Q4 Deirdre wants to find out if a soluble compound contains **chloride**, **bromide** or **iodide ions**. Explain how she could do this.

....

....

....

Q5 Complete the following symbol equations for reactions involved in **negative ion** tests.

a) $Ag^+_{(aq)} + \text{..............} \rightarrow AgCl_{(s)}$

b) $2HCl_{(aq)} + Na_2CO_{3(s)} \rightarrow 2NaCl_{(aq)} + \text{..............}_{(l)} + \text{..............}_{(g)}$

c) $\text{..............} + \text{..............} \rightarrow BaSO_{4(s)}$

Mixed Questions — Chemistry 3b

Q1   **Aerobic respiration** is the process of breaking down food using oxygen to release energy.

sugar + oxygen ⟶ carbon dioxide + water + energy

a)   Is this an **exothermic** or an **endothermic** reaction? Explain your answer.

....

b)   Choose the correct words to complete this statement about the above equation.

> The energy needed to **break** the bonds in the reactants is **greater than / less than** the energy released when the bonds in the products are **formed**.

c)   Describe one method that could be used to find the amount of energy in a food or a fuel.

....

....

d)   A 0.5 g sample of sugar is burned and releases enough energy to raise the temperature of 100 g of water by 15 °C. Calculate the energy produced per gram of sugar.

Use: $Q = mc\Delta T$.
The specific heat capacity of water is 4.2 J.

....

....

Q2   Stanley is trying to identify a mystery substance.

First he adds a few drops of sodium hydroxide solution to a solution of the mystery compound.

a)   What result would you expect Stanley to see if the mystery compound contained Fe^{2+} ions?

....

...and add a splash of $CaSO_4$, with a dollop of $MgBr_2$ and a dash of Worcester sauce...

b)   In fact, a blue precipitate forms. What can Stanley conclude?

....

c)   Write down an **ionic equation** for the formation of this blue precipitate.

....

d)   Stanley suspects that his compound is a sulfate. Describe a test he could do to see if he's right.

....

....

e)   Stanley does the test for a sulfate, and sees a white precipitate form in the solution.

Write down the formula of Stanley's mystery compound. ....

Mixed Questions — Chemistry 3b

Q3   The diagram shows the progress of a reaction which was carried out twice, once with a **catalyst** and once without.

a)   Label the **overall energy change** of the reaction with the symbol ΔH.

b)   Label the activation energy for reaction B on the graph.

c)   Which reaction used a **catalyst**, A or B? ....

d)   Does the graph represent an exothermic or an endothermic reaction?

....

Q4   Which ions would give the following results?

a)   Red colour in a flame test. ....

b)   Releases a gas that turns limewater cloudy when added to an acid. ....

c)   Forms a brown precipitate when NaOH solution is added. ....

d)   Forms a white precipitate after dilute HCl followed by $BaCl_2$ is added. ....

Q5   During a titration, 20 cm³ of 0.5 mol/dm³ sodium hydroxide solution was used to neutralise 25 cm³ of hydrochloric acid.

a)   In a titration experiment, suggest an **indicator** to use with HCl.

....

b)   What is the **concentration** of the acid, in:

i) moles per dm³?

....

....

....

....

ii) grams per dm³?

....

....

....

CAW44